ZOOMING WITH THE PAST

MARLENE ZAEDYAN

ISBN: 979-8-218-97941-6

DISCLAIMER

This book is a work of biographical fiction. While inspired by the author's own life experiences and relationships, the names and certain details of the characters have been altered to protectthe privacy of those involved.

The events, conversations, and interactions depicted are a mix offactual recollections and fictionalized elements. Any similarities to actual persons, living or deceased, are purely coincidental. Theauthor has exercised creative license to craft a narrative that reflects the essence of her memories and explores universal themes of friendship, self-discovery, and the human condition.

This book is not meant to serve as a precise factual account butas a heartfelt exploration of the author's personal journey, interpreted through the lens of her imagination and artistic expression. Readers should approach the content with the understanding that, while rooted in reality, "Zooming with the Past" is a work of literary fiction that artfully blends truth with the author's creative vision.

DEDICATION

I dedicate this book to all women who are unbounded in their power, whose tenacity clears a paththrough challenges, and whose quest for happiness isan exploration of who they are. The tale of your life is partly written by your resilience, whether you walk alone or with a partner. In every chapter, you break down walls, defy expectations, and bravely and gracefully put your goal first. This commitment celebrates the beauty of your path to inner tranquilityand fulfillment and your unflinching will.

CONTENTS

PROLOGUE:

Remember when we were kids and sci-fi shows like Star Trek and Land of the Giants held us spellbound? Beaming to distant planets, tackling challenges, and searching for a new home like Earth were all so captivating. We were glued to those episodes.

Those shows felt like messages from the future, like they were trying to awaken us to today's realities. Our planet is hurting. It's suffering from the injustices we've inflicted. The enemies? They're the ones tearing apart our Earth—cutting down forests, poisoning her, and choking her with pollution.

In the end, our actions bring about consequences. The most glaring one today? Viruses. We've flipped the script. We, the predators, have become the prey. Our impact on the environment has stirred dormant dangers, and now, viruses are our common enemy. COVID-19 is just one example; more may follow.

It's a wake-up call to the consequences of our actions, the need for balance, and the importance of rethinking our relationship with the planet. And it's not just a story; it's our reality, asking us to find harmony in a world we've disrupted.

Let's reflect on our past dreams of interstellar adventures and use that imagination to tackle the genuine challenge of preserving our one and only home, Earth. We can change our course to restore and protect our planet. The lessons of these sci-fi tales can guide us toward a brighter future. We can be the heroes of our own story, working together to heal our world, to mend the damage, and to ensure a harmonious coexistence with nature.

By learning from our past mistakes and acknowledging our role in the well-being of our planet, we have the power to rewrite the narrative. With science, innovation, and a shared commitment to environmental stewardship, we can embark on a new adventure where the harmony between humanity and nature becomes a reality, not just a sci-fi dream. It's a challenge but also an opportunity that we must embrace for the sake of future generations and the survival of our precious Earth.

As the pandemic raged across the globe, I found myself confined within the walls of my own home.

The world I once knew, with its bustling streets and vibrant gatherings, had become a distant memory. Zoom and Facetime became the norm, replacing family gatherings for holidays and serving as my virtual office.

I couldn't help but wonder about the future, particularly my grandchildren and the generations to come. I've lived a life filled with cherished memories of travel, friends' warmth, and family's embrace. But what kind of world have we bequeathed to our descendants? Will they have the chance to create similar memories?

I found solace in my memories during those trying times. They resurfaced, comforting me during my confinement. I was grateful for the stories I could share, a testament to a well-lived life. My days unfolded slowly, oscillating between the confines of my kitchen and the view from my window. Gazing into the mirror was an exercise I often avoided, as it revealed the swiftness with which time had passed.

My living room window faced small woods, which provided a different shade of green through the changing seasons and introduced me to various species. The most exquisite gift was the scent of freshness that wafted in whenever I opened the window. This connection to nature allowed me to feel the world's vastness and our Creator's presence.

In the midst of isolation, these reflections on memories, family, and nature helped me find meaning and gratitude. It's only natural to worry about what the future holds. Still, the resilience and adaptability of each generation, including our own, give hope that they will navigate the challenges that come their way, just as we did. Through the stories we share, we can bridge the gap between generations, passing on our wisdom and experiences to guide them through the everchanging journey of life.

Book I

CHAPTER I

ECHOES OF FRIENDSHIP: A JOURNEY THROUGH MEMORY AND SOLITUDE

Life lays down harsh demands, creating severe conditions, to test our suitability for growth and strength, though we cannot blame Life for that.

In the quiet moments of solitude, I find myself consumed by nostalgia, reflecting on the vibrant memories of my youth and the friends who once filled my days. Gone are the glories and the dark nights, replaced by the monotony of pacing back and forth within the confines of my home. More than a year has passed, stolen from us by circumstances beyond our control. Who is to blame? Perhaps we all bear a share of responsibility.

Seeking solace, I retreat to my living room, where the flickering flames of the fireplace offer a comforting reprieve. As I gaze into the fire, I am reminded of a poignant scene from Fahrenheit 451, where fire symbolizes perpetual motion and destruction. Its mesmerizing dance of colors draws me into a trance, evoking emotions ranging from passion to anger before transporting me to a realm of enchantingfantasies.

Throughout the trials of the pandemic year, a window emerged as my sanctuary, a portal to a treasure trove of memories. With each gentle rustle of leaves, my mind embarked on a journey back to a bygone era, to moments cherished deeply in my heart. The outside world seemed to fade away, and I willingly surrenderedto these recollections.

In those moments, every deep breath felt like a sip from the fountain of youth, and when I closed my eyes,I was transported to a time of unadulterated joy. Memories flooded my mind, each imbued with its unique blend of emotions. Tears were shed for lost loved ones, laughter shared with friends, and moments of sheer bliss filled my heart with warmth.

But amidst the nostalgia, there was also a profoundsense of longing. Longing for the days when life wassimpler, when worries were few and far between. Longing for the embrace of loved ones, for the soundof laughter echoing through the halls.

In those days, we were four friends, Anna, Fadia, Mariam and me. Anna and I resembled strikingly, like two peas in a pod. Fadia had long, dark hair and captivating black eyes, and Mariam had a fragile staturewith brown hair.

Within the realm of my dearest memories, the presence of my beloved friends painted my world with vivid hues. Our friendship was an unbreakable bond, a testament to the enduring power of true companionship. One memory shines with particular brilliance, whisking me away to the river's shores.

The four of us are running along the river in these treasured recollections. The sun caressed our skin with its warm embrace, and the mountain breeze playfullytousled our hair, imbuing us with a sense of boundless freedom and youthful exuberance.

Firstly, Mariam came to my mind. As I continued tobask in the warmth of the fireplace, memories of Mariam flooded my mind like an ember igniting a flame. Like the sparks dancing in the fire, her hair was a golden cascade of waves, complemented by her dark brown eyes that sparkled with mischief and merriment.Mariam was more than a friend; she was a kindred spirit, a companion in the childhood journey.

We shared everything, from dolls to clothes, dreams to secrets. Our days were filled with laughter and adventure as we ran, biked, and swam together. In theclassroom, we sat side by side, sharing a desk and whispering about our hopes and dreams for the future.

But our escapades to the nearby pond forged the strongest memories. With giggles of excitement, we would sneak out on our bikes, the cool breeze tousling our hair as we raced toward our secret hideaway. There,amidst the tranquil waters and lush greenery, we wouldswim and frolic, reveling in the freedom of youth. Andas if nature itself conspired to add to our joy, we wouldpluck wild berries from the bushes, filling our small bucket with the sweet bounty of the earth.

Those moments were pure magic, etched into the fabric of my being as cherished memories of a time when life was simpler, and friendship knew no bounds. Mariam may have drifted from my daily life, but in the flickering flames of the fireplace, her spirit burned bright, a reminder of the enduring bonds of childhood camaraderie.

As I stood by my window, lost in the reverie of childhood memories, the world outside seemed to transform before my eyes. The trees towered higher, their leaves ablaze with vibrant colors that danced in the sunlight. Each day held the promise of new adventures, and every night was a prelude to another thrilling escapade.

With a cup of warm cup of coffee, cradled in my hands, I found myself drawn to the sight of a curious squirrel, its eyes wide with fear and wonder as our gazes met. Memories of Mariam came flooding me like a rush of emotions from a distant past.

I recalled the day when Mariam, overcome by distress, had fled from me, seeking solace in the shelter of a nearby cavern by the pond. Despite my pleas to wait, she disappeared into the darkness, leaving me to follow in her wake.

Inside the cavern, I found her huddled in the shadows; her body wracked with sobs as she grappled with her inner turmoil. Try as I might, I could not soothe her troubled soul nor ease the storm of fear within her.

At that moment, Mariam seemed like a fragile vine, battered by the winds of adversity, her spirit bent but unbroken. And though I could not erase her pain or banish her fears, I offered what comfort I could, tenderly stroking her hair as we emerged from the cavern, united in our shared vulnerability and resilience.

From that day on, Mariam was never the same. The once joyful and talkative girl seemed to fade into the background, replaced by a shadow of her former self. We were just eleven years old at the time, but the weight of that moment seemed to linger, casting a somber pall over our friendship.

CHAPTER II

MARIAM

"They say time heals all wounds, but that presumes the source of the grief is finite,"

Wrote Cassandra Clare in Clockwork Prince. This sentiment resonates deeply with Mariam's story.

After that fateful day by the pond, my childhood friend Mariam withdrew into herself. She never spoke of what troubled her, but the change in her wasevident. Her once bright demeanor dimmed, her grades plummeted, and her physical appearance mirrored the turmoil within. It became clear thatsomething profound had shaken her to the core.

Despite her silence, our bond endured, albeit in a different form. Mariam became like a shadow, always present but never fully seen. We communicated through unspoken gestures, our connection transcending the need for words. I watched as she carried the weight of her pain, her youthful spirit gradually fading into the background.

At just thirteen years old, Mariam seemed to age beyond her years, resigned to a life devoid of joy and beauty. Time continued its relentless march forward, but for Mariam, it stood still, trapping her in a cycle of despair. I longed to lift her from the depths of her anguish, to show her that there was still hope beyond the darkness that enveloped her.

But how could she see the light when trapped at the bottom of a pit? I yearned for her to trust me, to reach out and grasp the hand of salvation I offered. Together, we could navigate the healing journey, emerging stronger on the other side.

I waited patiently, biding my time until the moment felt right. It was as if a switch had been flipped in my mind, a determination to intervene and pull Mariam from the depths of her despair. The years of her silent suffering could no longer be tolerated; action was necessary.

One late afternoon, I decided to visit her. As I approached her house, a car parked in the driveway, a sign of life amidst the stillness. With each step toward the front door, my heart pounded with anticipation. I knocked, and after a few moments, Mariam answered.

Her appearance shocked me to the core. She stood before me like an ice sculpture, her skin pale and translucent, veins protruding like tree roots. Yet, behind her icy facade, I sensed a flicker of warmth, a glimmer of hope.

Wordlessly, Mariam stepped aside to let me in, and I followed her into the quiet confines of her home. Something felt off, a palpable tension hanging in the air. I inquired about her mother, to which Mariam replied that she was out grocery shopping. But the stillness enveloped the house spoke volumes, hintingdeeper hidden secrets.

As I entered Mariam's home, the atmosphere felt heavy with unspoken tension. Her father sat on the couch, a drink in hand, his gaze fixed on me with anintensity that sent a shiver down my spine. Mariam'seyes darted away, unable to meet my own.

"Please, follow me," she whispered, her voice barely audible above the silence that hung in the air.

I couldn't help but notice the stark changes in her room as we walked. The once vibrant walls now laybare, devoid of the posters and trinkets that once adorned them. It was as if a piece of her childhood hadbeen stripped away, leaving behind only echoes of the past.

"What happened?" I ventured, unable to contain my curiosity. "Did you decide to grow up suddenly?"

Mariam's silence spoke volumes, her downcast eyes betraying the turmoil within her. We sat on her bed, and I reached out to hold her hand, desperate for some semblance of understanding.

But her response shattered my heart into a million pieces. "I'm okay," she murmured, her voice barely audible. "Please don't ask me to say anything. You're my dearest friend, but please respect my silence. And... please don't come to my house anymore."

Her words felt like a dagger to my soul, a rejection cutmore profoundly than I could have imagined. With aheavy heart, I nodded in acquiescence, masking my pain behind a facade of understanding.

As I left Mariam's house, a cloud of doubts and unanswered questions loomed over me. I tried deciphering the mystery surrounding her, but each presumption led me further into a labyrinth of uncertainty. Despite my best efforts, I couldn't shakethe unease that gnawed at my insides, leaving me haunted by thoughts of my dear friend.

CHAPTER III

MOTHER'S DAY

Mother's Day always carried a profound significanceat our school, highlighted by a captivating performance by the legendary singer Fairuz. As was customary, students queued up according to their grades,anticipation mingling with the air as we awaited the day's festivities. But amidst the excitement, a palpable heaviness seemed to linger, casting a shadow over theusual jubilant atmosphere.

Standing ahead of me in line, Mariam bore the weightof this melancholy, her demeanor betraying a deep sadness that tugged at my heartstrings. Fairuz's melodic voice filled the corridors, but instead of invoking joy, itseemed to evoke a sense of mourning, like the solemnity of a funeral or the contemplative mood of Good Friday. While some of my classmates reminiscedfondly, others wrestled with guilt over past rifts with their mothers, and a few seemed entirely detached from the day's significance. But Mariam's tear-stained cheeks caught my attention, stirring a surge of concern within me.

It had been a while since I'd seen her mother, and asudden realization struck me like a lightning bolt. Could it be that her mother had passed away? Or was there something else, something deeply troubling, lurking beneath the surface? Unable to ignore Mariam's evident distress, I anxiously awaited the coffee break, my mind swirling with apprehensive thoughts.

When the bell finally rang, signaling the break, I wasted no time pulling Mariam aside, urging her to stay with me in the classroom. With a sense of urgency gnawing at me, I confronted her, my voice trembling with concern as I implored her to share the burdens weighing on her soul. And then, finally, she spoke, her words carrying the weight of emotions too heavy to bear alone. Still, she kept her silence.

As we sat there, enveloped in a heavy silence, I knew that no amount of words or gestures could erase the pain Mariam had endured. But I vowed to stand by her side, to offer whatever support and comfort I could, hoping to ease her burden, if only for a moment.

Driven by a newfound determination to uncover the mysteries surrounding Mariam's transformation, I embarked on a quest for answers. Like unraveling the final thread of a yarn, each revelation brought a sense of relief and clarity, guiding me closer to the truth.

On a Friday night, I knew my parents would spend their weekend at my aunt's house. I took this as a signal to get closer to Mariam, so I invited her to have lunch with me on Saturday.

As the weekend unfolded, Mariam and I found ourselves on the balcony, surrounded by the tantalizing aroma of our favorite appetizers. Yet, despite the warmth of the afternoon and the delicious spread before us, Mariam's demeanor remained somber, her eyes distant and laden with unspoken sorrow.

The transition from the bustling school week to the quiet embrace of the weekend usually brought solace, but this time was different. There was a palpable tension between us, an unspoken barrier that seemed to distance us from the carefree companionship we once shared. Mariam's gaze remained fixed on the ground, her silence echoing the weight of her hidden turmoil.

I had prepared the appetizers with care, hoping to provide some semblance of comfort to my friend, but even the delicious spread failed to lift the veil of melancholy that shrouded Mariam's spirit. She thanked me for the gesture, her words tinged with a hint of sadness that tugged at my heartstrings.

To lighten the mood, I suggested we toast our friendship, invoking memories of ancient celebrations we had learned about in history class. A fleeting smile graced Mariam's lips at the memory, a flicker of the joyous spirit she once possessed.

As we indulged in the food and (sneaked)wine, the tension between us dissipated, replaced by a sense of ease and familiarity. The music provided a soothing backdrop to our conversation, gradually coaxing Mariam out of her shell.

Mariam seemed to relax with each sip of wine, her guard lowering as the alcohol worked its magic. I waited patiently, knowing the right moment would come for her to unburden herself.

Then, With the gentle strains of music filling the room and the warmth of wine coursing through her veins, she was suddenly seized by a surge of energy.Rising from her seat, she moved with the grace and poise of a seasoned ballerina, her body effortlessly gliding across the floor. With each twirl and twist, itwas as though she was shedding the weight of her burdens and sorrows, allowing herself to be consumed by the liberating embrace of the dance.

Her movements were mesmerizing, a testament to the power of music and motion to uplift the spirit. She spun and whirled with abandon, the room alive with the rhythmic cadence of her steps. But as she reachedthe peak of her dance, a wave of emotion overcame her, and she collapsed to the floor in a cascade of tears,her descent reminiscent of the tragic elegance of theblack swan.

Her hair, once a dark veil framing her face, now spread out like a mantle around her, a poignant symbolof her vulnerability and pain. Yet, even in her moment of anguish, there was a raw beauty to her vulnerability,a poignant reminder of the depth of human emotion.

As she lay there, crumpled on the floor, her tears mingling with the melody of the music, it was as thoughshe had released something within herself, a catharticrelease that spoke to the healing power of dance andmusic.

Finally, as she stood at the balcony fence, her hair shielding her face from view, I gently urged her to share her pain. I assured her of my unwavering support, encouraging her to trust our friendship as a source of solace and understanding.

Mariam took a deep breath. With a trembling voice, she began to unravel the layers of her suffering, each revelation a testament to the resilience of the human spirit in the face of adversity.

"My mother left us," she whispered, her voice trembling with emotion. "She ran off with someone else, leaving behind a shameful situation for my father and me."

As Mariam recounted her painful ordeal, my heart ached for her. To endure not only the abandonment of a parent but also to become the target of her father's misplaced anger and blame was a burden no one should have to bear. I struggled to find the right words to offer comfort, realizing that sometimes, silence speaks louder than words.

But then, Mariam hesitated before continuing, her voice barely above a whisper. "And... my father..." she trailed off, unable to bring herself to say the words. You know! So ashamed and broken.

As tears streamed down her cheeks, she shared her mother's heart-wrenching decision to leave her abusive husband for an old flame. The room was enveloped in a heavy silence, filled with the weight of betrayal and sorrow. Despite the overwhelming sadness, she bravely voiced her story, her voice trembling with emotion. In that moment, surrounded by understanding, she carried the burden of her pain.

CHAPTER IV

A MOTHER'S ESCAPE

*"Like a bird breaking free from its cage, a mother's escape
is not an act of abandonment, but a courageous flight towards
liberation, carrying the hopes of a brighter tomorrow."*

For years, Mariam had carried the weight of her family's struggles in silence, shielding me from the painful truth of her father's alcoholism and abusive behavior. It was a burden she bore alone, her youthful innocence tarnished by the harsh realities of her home life.

As Mariam recounted the gradual descent into darkness that had consumed her family, I listened with a heavy heart, grappling with the magnitude of her suffering. Her father, once introverted but not overtly cruel, had transformed into a volatile figure, his actions leaving a trail of destruction in their wake.

With each passing day, Mariam's mother bore the brunt of her husband's wrath, enduring verbal tirades and physical abuse that left her broken and sad. Mariam, powerless to intervene, could only watch as her mother retreated into isolation, seeking solace in the confines of their home.

The signs of her mother's unhappiness were unmistakable: neglected chores, abandoned meals, and a pervasive sense of despair that hung heavy in the air. Yet, despite her anguish, Mariam's mother remained steadfast in her silence, refusing to acknowledge the pain that threatened to consume her.

It was only in hindsight that Mariam began to piece together the fragments of her mother's unraveling. The subtle shifts in her demeanor, the fleeting moments of happiness that flickered across her face—each a clue to the turmoil brewing beneath the surface.

And then, one day, her mother was gone, leaving behind nothing but a note of apology and a declaration of love. In the wake of her departure, Mariam was left to grapple with the devastating reality of her mother's betrayal, struggling to make sense of the choices that had led her to this point.

But as Mariam recounted the events that had unfolded, a newfound understanding dawned on me. Behind her mother's actions lay a desperate bid for freedom, a courageous act of self-preservation in the face of overwhelming adversity.

Ultimately, Mariam's mother found the strength to break free from the chains that bound her, reclaiming her autonomy and forging a brighter future.

I felt a knot form in my stomach; my heart broke for her in a way I never thought possible. To suffer such betrayal and abuse at the hands of the very people who were supposed to love and protect her was beyond comprehension. And yet, she was bearing the weightof their sins on her fragile shoulders. And I felt angerand rage toward her mother.

As I embraced Mariam tightly, I realized the profound impact of trust and vulnerability. It was a testament to the strength of our friendship, forged through years of shared experiences and unwaveringsupport.

Yet, amidst the intimacy of our conversation, one detail remained conspicuously absent: Mariam had never confided in her mother about the abuse she suffered at the hands of her father. It was a silence bornof shame and fear, a burden she carried alone for fartoo long. And as I listened to her story, my heart achedwith the weight of her pain, knowing that no child should ever endure such cruelty in silence. But in that moment, surrounded by love and understanding, I vowed to stand by Mariam's side, offering her the unwavering support and compassion she deserved.

Thinking Looking back, I couldn't help but feel a pang of regret for my previous judgment of Mariam'smother. In my ignorance and anger, I failed to see beyond my assumptions and biases, missing the opportunity to truly understand Mariam's truth. Yet,even in my regret, I found solace in the realization that anger, when channeled constructively, can catalyze growth and self-discovery.

As Mariam's story drew close, a sense of regret washed over her. Then she

added,

If only I had been brave enough to speak the truth about my own father's abuse, perhaps our destinies would have taken a different course. But in the end, itwas a lesson learned—a reminder that silence can bejust as damaging as the pain it seeks to conceal.

She said, maybe she could have taken me with her.

MONDAY SCHOOL

Monday morning dawned with an unsettling absence—Mariam's empty desk was a stark reminder of her absence. As the days stretched into weeks, her mysterious disappearance weighed heavily on my mind, a puzzle with no solution in sight.

My concern for Mariam grew daily, overshadowing my ability to focus on anything else. I reached out to her home, only to be met with silence and uncertainty. Her father's cold demeanor offered no comfort; his callous dismissal left me adrift in a sea of unanswered questions.

As I grappled with the overwhelming sense of helplessness, I found solace in believing our connection transcended the physical realm. In the depths of my despair, I clung to the notion that Mariam would find her way back to me, guided by the invisible threads of our shared bond.

And then, just when I had begun to lose hope, a glimmer of light appeared in the darkness—a letter from Mariam, delivered by the hand of fate itself. With trembling hands, I tore open the envelope, eager to unravel the mysteries contained within its pages.

With each word, the puzzle pieces began to fall into place, vividly depicting Mariam's journey and trials. Her words carried the weight of her experiences, each sentence a testament to her resilience and strength in the face of adversity.

As I read her letter, I felt relief, knowing that she wassafe and our connection remained unbroken despite the miles separating us. One phrase that caught my attention was:

I HAD TO LEAVE. I am with my mother, safe.Until

we meet again.

With Love, Mariam.

At that moment, I realized that our bond was not defined by physical proximity but by the enduring power of friendship and love.

Though Mariam's whereabouts may have been a mystery, her presence remained palpable in my heart, aguiding light in the darkness that reminded me of thestrength found in our shared humanity. As I folded her letter and tucked it away, I knew our connection wouldendure, transcending time and distance to unite us again..

I never heard back from her.

ANNA

Our appearances were so remarkably similar that people often mistook Anna and me for sisters. At the same time, Fadia's long, dark hair and captivating black eyes added an intriguing contrast. We were a quartet, each with our unique voice, but together, we shared an unbreakable bond.

Our friendship was beyond mere companionship; it was a profound intertwining of hearts and minds. In the mosaic of shared experiences, I felt Anna's moments of joy and revealed in her successes, just as she did in mine. Our lives unfolded in the same city, within the confines of the same school, and through growing up together.

Anna's first love story, with its sweet promises, youthful hopes, and eventual heartache, is a chapter etched deeply in my memory that I longed to retell. In a world filled with shared secrets and the harmonious laughter of friendship, we faced the trials and tribulations of adolescence together.

Under the radiant, sunlit skies and amidst the soothing sounds of the mountains, these shared moments became indelible imprints in my memory, a testament to the enduring beauty of friendship, empathy, and unwavering mutual support. Like a timeless painting that captures the essence of fleeting moments, our friendship was boundless, much like the endless horizon of the ocean, embracing our hearts and minds in the symphony of shared laughter and shareddreams.

She entered the world of love as she approached her sixteenth year. Among all her young friends, she sawherself as the one who had been chosen. At that tender age, she felt like the luckiest girl in her class and amongall her peers. This unique experience was somethingshe cherished, and it filled her heart with pride and wonder.

Our school was nestled in a quaint village in Lebanonknown as Zahle, cradled in a valley encircled by majestic mountains. The town was a breathtaking sight, brilliantly white in the winter, and in the summer, it transformed into a lush green paradise. Abundant rivers meandered through the valley, and their melodious symphony and the echoes of nearby waterfalls serenaded the entire region. Zahle boasted numerous promenade spots and charming sidewalk cafes, known as cafe trottoir, where villagers gathered to share stories, laughter, and life.

Her house, perched upon a hill, was a living testamentto the passage of time. Its walls were crafted from ancient carved rocks, bearing witness to centuries gone by. In the yard, a blackberry tree stood to the left, its branches heavy with mature berries that had fallen. Intheir dried state, these berries resembled old,bittersweet tears, each carrying a history of poignantlove stories and untold tales.

The legend whispered of love's trials and triumphs, clandestine meetings under the blackberry tree, where secrets were exchanged, and hearts were laid bare. It spoke of stolen kisses in the moonlight, promises made and sometimes broken, and the ever-present, all-seeing eyes of the ancient rocks that watched over it all.

In this idyllic village of Zahle, where everyone was either family or foe, depending on the intricate tapestry of history woven between neighbors, Anna's journey into love was destined to be a tale of passion and heartache. The echoes of that time still reverberate through the valley, carried by the winds that sweep down from the surrounding mountains and rustle the leaves of the blackberry tree as if whispering the secrets of love to those who care to listen.

What I learned from the town folks about the legend was that,

Long long ago, in a village that time seemed to have forgotten, there stood a small, unassuming fountain beside a tree—the blueberry tree. This humble fountain was a lifeline for the villagers, a place where they came to fill their clay jugs with its cold, medicinal drinking water. But this place was more than a simple water source; it was known for something else—it was a sanctuary for love.

Here, beneath the branches of the blueberry tree, destiny had a way of weaving its intricate patterns. It was where young hearts would cross paths, sometimes by chance, and those chance encounters often transformed into passionate love affairs. *For others, it served as the backdrop for secret rendezvous, where stolen moments were shared away from prying eyes.*

The legend that would echo through the ages began on a rainy day. The heavens wept, and a young girl and a shepherd found themselves at the fountain as if by divine design.

Simultaneously. This girl and the shepherd's paths converged under the weeping sky, and a storm brewed on the horizon.

In the moment's urgency, the shepherd, a gentle soul with a heart as vast as the rolling hills, extended a hand of kindness. Together, they ran, each clutching a jug, but fate had other plans. The girl's jug slipped from her grasp, shattering into pieces on the ground. A pang of sadness filled her heart.

As the rain poured down in torrents, the storm raged around them. Lightning painted the sky, and thunder roared like a mighty beast. The girl's tear-streaked face glistened with raindrops, her sorrow hidden beneath the mask of falling rain. It was a moment of shared vulnerability, where the tempest mirrored the tumultuous emotions that swirled within her.

With her eyes cast downward, she silently wept, dreading the thought of returning home with empty hands, her father's wrath a looming shadow.

As the storm roared on, they waited together beneath the blueberry tree. The world outside was in chaos, but beneath its sheltering canopy, a seed had been planted—an unspoken promise, a relationship established by fate itself. Before she went, the shepherd gave her his jug.

In the days that followed, an irresistible force seemed to guide their destiny. Love blossomed beneath the watchful eyes of the blueberry tree, and their hearts beat in harmony with the rhythm of the village.

Their encounters grew more frequent, their love more profound. The shepherd, his attention often stolen by her radiant beauty, found himself distracted, almost losing some of his sheep to wayward thoughts. She, too, felt the irresistible pull, and her frequent outings left her father puzzled.

However, time has a way of revealing secrets, and the day arrived when her father's suspicions could no longer be ignored. He decided to follow her, determined to uncover the truth. With his own eyes, he witnessed his daughter in the company of a man beneath the blueberry tree. His anger surged like a storm, dark and foreboding.

He raced back home, his fury billowing around him like black clouds. From a distance, he watched his daughter return, her face radiant, her jug balanced on her shoulder. She sang a song of contentment, unaware of the tempest about to descend.

But her father's patience had reached its limit. Unable to contain his rage any longer, he ran towards her, his fury a force of nature. Trembling, she tried to defend herself, but her father's anger thundered, drowning her words.

As the legend goes, love does not bow to the will of fathers or the constraints of society. Neither she nor her beloved were willing to surrender their love. They continued to meet in secret, under the protective shadow of the blueberry tree, where their love flourished.

Their meetings became a lifeline, a refuge from the storm of disapproval that raged around them. They met at night, underthe soft glow of the moon, their whispered promises and stolen kisses a testament to the depth of their love.

However, one fateful night, her father noticed her absence, and, consumed by anger, he grabbed a machete and set out to find her. He discovered her beneath the blueberry tree, her lover by her side, bathed in the moon's silver light.

Blinded by rage and a misguided sense of honor, her father made a dreadful choice. He lunged, seized his daughter, and in a single, horrific act, he took her life. Her lover, overwhelmed with grief and shock, met the same tragic fate at the father's hand.

In his twisted belief, her father thought he was reclaiming and purifying his honor. He left a legacy of sorrow, and the blueberry tree bore witness to the tragedy. From that day forward, the tree's fruits were forever marked with a dark hue, a poignant reminder of the love story that had unfolded beneath its branches, a tale of love that had defied the storms of life and met a tragic end.

It stood as a silent sentinel, its branches heavy with sweet fruit, a living testament to a love that had weathered the storm and a sacrifice that had left an indelible mark on its very essence.

The house had a unique feature that left visitors breathless - forty uneven stairs leading up to the entrance. Climbing those stairs was an exercise, a tangible reminder of the effort it took to reach the sanctuary that was Anna's home. Each ascent left us breathless, not just from the physical exertion but from the anticipation of what lay at the top - the warmth of Anna's family, the comforting aroma of home-cooked meals, and the laughter that filled the rooms.

Once inside, the house revealed its modest but warm interior. It consisted of two bedrooms where dreams were woven and secrets shared. The walls bore witness to the quiet conversations, the whispered hopes, and the unspoken fears. The living room, at the heart of the home, featured a diesel stove that was more than just a source of heat; it was a symbol of comfort andtogetherness. Its steady glow mirrored the warmth that filled the family's hearts.

To the right, the kitchen stood, where the aroma offamily recipes filled the air. The clinking of pots andpans was a symphony of love and tradition, a reminderthat each meal was not just sustenance but a testament to their unity. And just outside, the bathroom served a singular purpose - for the release of intestinal food leftovers. It was a humble space, lacking the luxuries ofmodern living, but it was a place where privacy wasrespected and dignity was preserved.

There was no luxury of a shower in this humble abode. Instead, the family adhered to a once-a-weekcleansing ritual on Saturdays. Each of them takes hisprivate bath in a small, hot, portable aluminum tank or tub in one of the bedrooms. The anticipation of this sacred cleaning day was palpable. It wasn't just about physical cleanliness but a renewal of the spirit. The moments spent in that makeshift bath were washing away dirt and shedding the burdens of the week, emerging refreshed and rejuvenated.

These Saturday days served as an occasion forthorough cleaning throughout the house, from top tobottom. House, bath, shoe shine, and laundry - everything was meticulously attended to. It wasn't achore; it was a labor of love. The cleaning was a symbolic gesture of devotion to their home and respectfor the sacred space they had built together.

CHAPTER V

HER FAMILY

In the tapestry of Anna's life, her mother's choicesformed a brilliant, vivid thread of passion that weaved through every aspect of their existence. It was as though their family was a living canvas painted withbold strokes of determination and love. More than anobserver, Anna actively participated in this breathtaking masterpiece, absorbing the lessons of her mother's unwavering passion.

Her mother's remarriage was a practical solution and a defiant proclamation against despair. It was a boldstatement that life's challenges, no matter how daunting, could never smother the flames of hope andcompanionship. With each passing day, her mother'spassionate pursuit of happiness was a vibrant tapestryof resilience, showing that loneliness could never overshadow the brilliance of togetherness. This fiery spirit was a beacon, lighting up their lives.

In her youthful wisdom, Anna saw her mother's choice to remarry for companionship as embodying her spirit. It was a vivid reflection of a woman who dared to chart her own course, unburdened by the constraints of societal expectations and norms. It was the ultimate testament to living life with fierce determination.

Her acceptance and deep empathy for her mother's choices were born of her passion for understanding and supporting those she cherished. It was a love that blazed with intensity, a profound connection beyond blood ties. It was the kind of love that made her mother's boundaries, particularly Rule 1, not just a rule but a solemn promise to protect their relationships from external interference.

This rule was a sacred covenant that encapsulated the ardor her mother held for her children. It was a fortress built around their familial bonds, ensuring no force could undermine their profound connection. It was a reflection of the passionate love that bound them together.

Their most cherished moments unfolded around the card table. The laughter that filled the room and the spirited banter accompanying their playful card games ignited a fiery joy in Anna's soul. It wasn't just a smile of relief that graced her face but a radiant, passionate glow emanating from her core.

Anna's stepfather, a man of boundless generosity he treated her mother with respect. – he poured his heart and soul into their family. Love, respect, and passion were not mere words; they were the very heartbeat of their family. Within these boundaries of love and respect, their lives were infused with an electric intensity that was palpable to anyone who entered their home.

He didn't just share in the financial responsibilities; he shared in the emotional wealth of the family. Anna's mother found her refuge in the living room, and her hookah was an instrument of connection to the past.

The fragrant smoke became a conduit to the depths of her heart, carrying her away to the cherished memories of her departed husband. Time seemed to stop in that room, and it was as if their love had never truly faded.

Her emotions painted a vivid and passionate portrait on her face in moments of solitude. Crystal's tears bore witness to the depth of her sorrow, a testament to the intensity of her feelings. Yet, a radiant smile, as bright as the sun on a perfect summer day, transformed her countenance when she relived the joys of yesteryears. Like deep pools of emotion, her eyes were a testament to the passionate love that had defined her life. They shifted from a smoky gray to a fiery, passionate blue as her memories danced through them.

This was a family that lived with intensity, where each moment was an eruption of passion, and love was a force of nature that pulsed through their very souls.

In embracing their unwavering Catholic faith, the family found a profound spirituality that touched every facet of their existence. Sundays held a unique and spiritual significance that elevated their lives beyond the ordinary. As the melodious church bells echoed through the air, they believed their hearts harmonized with a higher calling, filling them with a deep sense of peace and reassurance, their faith unwavering in its ability to ward off malevolent forces and bless theirhome with divine protection.

CHAPTER VI

SUNDAY CHURCH

"A sanctuary of serenity, where the melody of prayersrises like incense, and the congregation gathers, eachthread of faith woven with hope and love."

On Sundays, the family gathered with great reverence, and the church's hallowed doors opened aportal to the spiritual realm. For Anna, it was a day oftranscendent experiences, a journey beyond the confines of her everyday existence. As she stepped intothe sanctuary, she immediately connected to the divine.It was a time of spiritual reflection and the creation of life stories deeply rooted in faith.

The serenity of the church's ambiance had a mesmerizing effect, and Anna often found herself in a state of profound spiritual communion. Among the sacred elements of the service, the hymns and Gregorian music were particularly enchanting, like angelic voices that carried her to celestial heights. Inthose moments, she felt as if she were dancing with theangels, enveloped in the loving embrace of spiritual devotion, a harmonious fusion of her soul with the divine.

Even amidst the solemn church service, Anna found moments of distraction as her curious eyes roamed over the diverse congregation. Her favorite spot was tucked away in the very last row, affording her a unique view of every churchgoer. With a fresh and youthful perspective, she couldn't resist the urge to observe and playfully assess them – their clothing choices, expressions, and even how they walked. Occasionally, a suppressed giggle would escape her lips, earning her some bemused glances from fellow worshippers. Nevertheless, these small moments of amusement made time seem quicker, gently ushering in another ordinary Monday at school.

I fondly remember how, during our Monday breaks, we eagerly gathered around Anna to hear her lighthearted and often comical descriptions of the churchgoers. Her knack for turning their idiosyncrasies into entertaining anecdotes never failed to bring smiles to our faces. Through her playful perspective, the congregation transformed into a cast of charming characters, making our Monday gatherings all the more enjoyable.

One Sunday, a young man entered the church. He had no inkling that his life was about to take an unexpected turn. With reverence, he made his way to a vacant seat right in front of Anna, who was already seated. She was lost in her usual daydreams, the soft hymns washing over her like a gentle tide. Sunlight streamed through the stained glass windows, casting colorful patterns on the wooden pews.

The service began with the choir's ethereal voices filling the sanctuary with a sense of divine presence. During this harmonious moment, a warm breeze embraced Anna, gently coaxing her back to the present. To her, it felt like a loving angel was whispering softly in her ear, urging her to lend her voice to the choir. Anna had always possessed a voice that could only be described as angelic. As she began to sing, the beauty of her voice unfurled, filling the sacred space with a celestial resonance that seemed to transcend the earthly realm. Her songs were like prayers, offered to the heavens, and touched the hearts of everyone present. During these moments, her daydreams dissolved like morning mist, leaving her fully immersed in the enchanting music.

Unbeknownst to Anna, her voice had captured the congregation's hearts and drawn the young man's attention. Mesmerized, he turned his head to trace the source of the enchanting sound, his curiosity piqued by the exquisite melody that filled the air.

He beheld a captivating voice and a vision of beauty that left him utterly spellbound. Anna was a radiant figure, her long, flowing hair glistening like spun gold, her high cheekbones sculpting her face with grace, and her hazel eyes, deep and expressive, seemed to hold within them the secrets of a thousand lifetimes. Her skin was like porcelain, flawless and inviting.

For the 25-year-old man, it felt as though he had just encountered his first angel. The beauty of her voice and the exquisite vision before him intertwined in a profound and heart-stirring way, igniting emotions within him that he couldn't explain. It was a moment when the sacred and the earthly met, and he found himself deeply moved and enthralled by the enchantingmusic and the ethereal beauty of Anna.

She was, without a doubt, a dreamer, just as quiet and introverted as we both were. Her daily journey to school was like a pilgrimage through the corridors ofher imagination, transporting her to different realms and realities. During these solitary walks, she seemed almost somnambulant, her mind lost in the labyrinth of her thoughts, her external surroundings a mere backdrop until the chorus of fellow students jolted her back to the earthly realm.

Her innate disposition was that of an observer, a role she played as masterfully in the schoolyard as she didat church on Sundays. Anna had a knack for noticingthe details of every student and teacher, her perceptive gaze piecing together the fragments of their stories as though she were an amateur detective. It was a skill thatextended into the classroom, where she'd sit with a thoughtful air, taking in her surroundings, cataloging the eccentricities of her peers, and weaving intricatenarratives about their lives.

Then, just as we did at church, we'd convene later to share our whimsical tales and laugh heartily at the scenarios we'd concocted. During these moments ofshared creativity, we forged bonds that would carry us through the ups and downs of our school days, unitedby our vivid imaginations and our shared love for weaving stories from the ordinary tapestry of life.

CHAPTER VII

FIRST LOVE

The story of Anna's blossoming love affair began on a day I remember vividly. It was a day when Anna dashed toward me, her eyes shining like stars and her smile lighting up the room. Her enthusiasm was so infectious that it was impossible not to get caught up in the moment. It was as though her heart, racing with excitement, had its own joyful melody. And so, on that day, the enchanting tale of Anna's love story began.

Let me tell you about Nathan, who would soon become inseparable from my dear friend Anna's life. Thanks to their thriving farming business, Nathan comes from a family that's got it pretty good. Their sprawling lands are filled with fruit trees and lush vegetable gardens. They're not just local bigwigs; their produce reaches markets far and wide.

Nathan is in charge of taking care of this green kingdom. So, you can guess that most of his year is spent under the sun, tending to their crops. That's why he sports this deep, sun-kissed tan that perfectly complements his striking features. Picture this: dark hair, a neatly groomed goatee, and eyes as deep and captivating as a starry night. He's pretty much the stuff of dreams for many.

Here's the twist: Nathan has this undeniable charmand is known for making a lasting impression on almost everyone he meets. But, when it comes to matters of the heart, he's always been one to tread carefully, avoiding any whirlwind romances.

All that changed on that particular Sunday, the dayAnna's voice first graced his ears. Like an enchanting siren's call, her singing possessed a haunting quality that refused to be ignored. Her voice, a sweet and soul stirring melody, occupied his thoughts until the following Sunday when he could no longer resist thepull. He felt like a sailor drawn into the ocean's depths,hypnotized by the mesmerizing song of a mermaid, unable to escape the allure of her voice.

The Sunday service commenced at 9:30, but for Nathan, the heart-pounding anticipation would beginlong before the clock struck the hour. As the weekend neared, he would stand before the mirror, ensuring thathe was presentable and irresistible to the captivatingmermaid who had stolen his thoughts and dreams. Doubts gnawed at him: Was she too young for him? Would she find him attractive?

Yet, the confidence that coursed through his veins was undeniable. He was convinced that no woman could possibly resist him that day. With one final glancein the mirror, a spritz of cologne to match the grand occasion, and a nervous but exhilarated smile, he dismissed himself from his reflection, ready to embark on this thrilling new chapter in the company of the captivating Anna.

On the third Sunday, something truly extraordinary happened. Nathan and Anna's silent connection, crafted over weeks of shared glances and unspoken yearning, had finally reached a pivotal moment.

As the church service drew close, they both found themselves lingering as if caught in a moment too precious to end. Anna had made it her habit to stay behind, waiting until the last churchgoer had departed. For her, those were precious moments, stolen seconds to be close to him. Nathan had reasons to remain, his gaze locked onto Anna as if under a spell.

A tension of longing and anticipation hung like a warm, inviting breeze in the air. With every passing Sunday, their silent connection had deepened as if their souls had found their perfect harmony. They were like two symphonies playing in unison, and a wordless, beautiful melody surrounded them.

Nathan, emboldened by the moment, felt a surge of courage. As Anna rose from her seat, he mirrored her actions. The subtle fragrance of his cologne, as enchanting as his presence, enveloped her like a gentle caress. Anna felt drawn to him, helpless against the magnetic pull they shared.

In that sacred space, amidst the hushed serenity of the church, they forged a connection that transcended words. It was as if their souls had spoken in the silent language of the heart, and both understood the unspoken promise that hung in the air.

With one final, lingering gaze and a tender smile, Nathan departed, vanishing among the parked cars. Anna watched him go, her heart fluttering with the promise of the coming Sundays, where their unspoken connection would undoubtedly blossom into something more profound.

Anna floated back home, carried by an invisible breeze, light as a feather and dancing with the wind.

The lingering scent of Nathan's cologne surrounded her like a cherished secret, accompanying her to her doorstep. Suddenly, her house felt like a haven. Every piece of furniture, every corner of the familiar space, seemed to exude a newfound charm. She touched them as if they were precious treasures, and she moved about with the grace and joy of a princess in her enchanted castle.

Her younger siblings observed her with wide-eyed wonder, their curious gazes seeking answers for this unusual behavior and the source of her radiant happiness.

Love was the answer. Anna had fallen in love for the first time, and her heart was aflutter with an emotion that can only be experienced once. In her dreams, colorful butterflies danced gracefully around her head, symbols of transformation and rebirth. It was as though they were heralding a new chapter in her life, bidding farewell to her teenage years and ushering in the era of womanhood.

Some nights, as she drifted into dreams, she ran through a field of wildflowers, each bloom celebrating her newfound love. The world seemed to be in harmony with her heart's desires, and her dreams vividly depicted the love that had captured her youthfulheart.

Gradually, Anna inched closer to Nathan. What hadbegun as a mere exchange of glances and a few words had now evolved into a budding romance. She beganto accept his offers of rides, and soon, they were spending leisurely afternoons strolling together.

Anna skipped school occasionally, preferring the company of the man who had captured her heart. Every moment with him felt like a slice of heaven onearth.

A handful of her closest friends were privy to her secret relationship with Nathan. They, too, were adolescents teetering on the cusp of love and adulthood, and they couldn't help but envy the happiness and excitement that seemed to radiate fromAnna. At times, they even conspired to help her findways to meet Nathan secretly, covering for her whenneeded.

But youth, like a rose-tinted dream, often blinds us to the complexities of life. In their innocence, theybelieved that love and joy were endless and that life wasan unending parade of happiness. They wove dreams upon their first love, hearts caged and yearning for the freedom love promised.

In her dreams, she was confident that Nathan, her prince, would soon sweep her off her feet with a proposal. Her vivid imagination painted a picture of their future home, complete with perfect furnishings, a cozy bedroom, plush bath towels, and her gracefully navigating the kitchen, preparing his favorite dishes while dancing in pure delight.

However, as time passed, the reality began to divergefrom her cherished dreams.

Nathan's visits became less frequent, and his calls dwindled in number. Some days, he would blatantlyignore her calls and attend church with decreasing regularity. Anna sensed something was amiss, but the nature of the problem eluded her. For the very first time, she experienced a strange, painful sensation in herchest, a tightness that left her breathless and in turmoil.

Two long, agonizing weeks stretched by without any word from Nathan. It was a period filled with heartache and fear, as if she were constantly gasping forair, her world closing in around her. As the rain pattered against the windowpane, Anna sat curled upon her couch, lost in the pages of her favorite novel.

It was a serene Tuesday afternoon, the kind that begged for quiet reflection. Little did she know that unexpected news would soon shatter the tranquility.

In the course of our lives, a pivotal occasion occurred.Nathan's impending marriage was exposed through whispers carried on the winds of local gossip, a revelation with serious ramifications. Throughout this unfolding drama, Anna, a dear friend, was ignorant of the planned union. It was incumbent to me, as both confidant and bearer of truth, to ensure she heard it from a reliable source before it reached her ears through less respectful avenues. Thus, with a heavy heart and a sense of obligation, I accepted the task of sensitively communicating the news, knowing that in the world of friendship, transparency must always prevail.

Shock and dismay swept over her, threatening to consume her completely. As the news weighed on her, Anna became bewildered and sad. She couldn't believe the future she had imagined with Nathan was slipping through her fingers, replaced by the brutal reality of his upcoming marriage to someone else.

Memories filled her head like a never-ending tide— moments shared, promises made, and dreams weaved together. She recalled their laughing, whispered confidences, and sweet gestures that once gave her hope. But now, those recollections felt like cruel taunts, teasing her with the sharp contrast between what had been and what would be.

With shaking lips and tears in her eyes, she struggled with the terrible sense of loss and betrayal that threatened to swallow her. Nathan, how could he have withheld this from her? Did their bond mean nothing to him?

In the midst of her anguish, Anna experienced a flood of conflicting emotions—heartbreak mixed with fury, longing intermingled with a desperate need for closure. She wanted to approach Nathan and demand an explanation for his betrayal, but a part of her feared the grief such a confrontation would undoubtedly cause.

With a sad heart, Anna understood she had a choice: hold to the vestiges of a love that had already faded or summon the strength to carve a new route forward, free of the ghosts of the past. But for the time being, in the privacy of her agony, she allowed herself to lament the loss of what may have been, the love that had been lost to fate's harsh hands.

CHAPTER VIII
LOVE

Love is a multifaceted force, tender and challenging by turns. It beckons us with an irresistible allure, tugging at the very essence of our being. It takes us on a transformative journey, sometimes as gentle as a warm breeze and sometimes as formidable as a mountain to climb. Love can crown us with the intoxicating joy of shared moments, yet it has the power to crucify us with the searing pain of loss.

The entirety of the concise letter left Anna in stunned disbelief. It was as though her entire love story had come to an abrupt, unceremonious end within the confines of that plain white envelope. Her mind raced, searching for a rational explanation for this bewilderingturn of events. It couldn't be real; it must be a mistake, a cruel joke played at her expense. She looked around, her surroundings suddenly alien, as if the whole world had crumbled into an eerie silence.

"Why? How?" The questions reverberated in her mind like an unending, tormenting refrain. The veryground beneath her feet seemed to tremble in response to the earthquake that had torn through her heart, leaving her world in ruins.

Hours passed, each one heavier and more agonizingthan the last. She sat in stunned silence, tears eludingher as if her ability to weep had been stolen. Her mindfelt trapped in a suffocating fog, and a sickening nauseachurned within her. She was adrift in her own life, amere spectator to the unfolding tragedy as if watchinga heart-wrenching drama play out on a distant stage.

Amid this emotional tempest, one primal instinct remained — the overwhelming need to escape. Annayearned to run, to flee to a place where the torment couldn't reach her, where the wounds inflicted by this letter might one day heal.

The news of Nathan's forthcoming wedding sweptthrough our small city like a thunderclap. As the word spread, an eerie darkness engulfed the once beautiful valley where Anna resided. The very essence of nature rebelled against the injustice as waterfalls dried up, theirgentle cascades silenced, and the vibrant green of themountains withered into a somber, ashen hue. Even the sun, a constant presence in the azure sky, coweredbehind thick, brooding clouds as if the heavens were unwilling to bear witness to Anna's inevitable anguish.

In the confines of her room, she was a prisoner toher own sorrow. She sought solace in the comforting embrace of darkness, drawing the curtains tight and allowing the shadows to envelop her. There, she counted the days to that fateful, gloomy Sunday, every passing hour echoing with the weight of her despair.

As her friend, I could do little to lift her spirits; thewounds were too fresh, the pain too raw. I left her be,knowing that time alone could mend even the deepest wounds. But the relentless march of life carried on, indifferent to her suffering. Days turned into weeks, the present slipped into the past, and the future danced its way into the present — and then, too, slipped intothe annals of the past. Yet, this particular Sunday refused to be relegated to the past; it remained etched in Anna's heart as an unhealed wound.

When that heart-wrenching Sunday arrived, Anna woke with a heavy heart and prepared herself for church, although it was no ordinary Sunday service. This time, she was bound for the church where Nathan's wedding would occur. She needed to confront the truth and witness the inevitable with herown eyes.

The weather that day seemed to mirror her profoundsadness and distress as the heavens wept with heavy rain and thunderstorms, each downpour echoing her inner turmoil. Anna sought refuge behind the massive wooden entry door, her pulse pounding in time with the rolling thunder. She peered into the dimly lit interior of the church, where the sight of the couple standing before the altar was an image etched into her soul.

As the father recited the commitment question, Nathan responded with an infuriatingly radiant smile, uttering the words, "Yes, I do." The priest'sproclamation, "You may kiss your bride," resoundedthrough the church, piercing Anna's heart like a jaggedblade. In that agonizing moment, a scream of sheer anguish and rage burst forth from her, tearing through the solemn silence. She fled from the church, her sobs blending with the relentless rain as she retraced her steps to her home.

There, she sought refuge beneath the sheltering branches of the blueberry tree; their leaves weighed down by the deluge. The tree offered her solace as she wept, her cries merging with the fallen berries, creating a somber pool at her feet. The earth seemed to weep alongside her as if nature was mourning the tragic unraveling of her love story.

She sat in profound silence for hours as if an abyss had swallowed her very being. Her siblings and I gathered around her, their voices filled with worry and confusion, but Anna's mind was a desolate void, an echoing emptiness where thoughts and emotions had been banished. Her vacant gaze remained fixed on the abyss, impenetrable and disconnected from the world.

Under the sheltering canopy of the blueberry tree, she found herself drawn to the legend that clung to its branches. The tragic tale of the star-crossed lovers, torn asunder by the cruel hand of the young girl's vengeful father, resonated deeply within her. In the shadows of her own heartbreak, Anna yearned for a conclusion to her story that mirrored the mournful fate of the girl in that sorrowful legend. The world around her seemed to share in her despair as if the very elements wept alongside her, and the air was heavy with the weight of her desolation.

Anna's life became a tapestry of solitude and silent suffering. The world outside carried on, oblivious to the tempest raging within her. Every day was a struggle, a relentless battle with the anguish that had taken residence in her heart. Her dreams, once filled with hope and youthful optimism, had given way to the bleak landscape of disappointment.

She would often gaze at her reflection in the mirror, seeing not the radiant girl she used to be but the shadow of her former self. Her body had the frailty of one who had weathered too many storms; her spirit was weighed down by the gravity of her heartache. The sparkle in her eyes had dimmed, and her laughter had become a distant memory, like the faint echo of a melody that once brought joy.

Even the blueberry tree, once a source of solace, seemed to mourn alongside her. Its branches, once lush with the promise of sweet fruit, now hung heavy and burdened, mirroring Anna's sense of loss. The legend of the star-crossed lovers had taken on new meaning for her, and she found herself identifying with the tragic young girl forsaken by the world.

Her days were marked by a quiet routine, punctuated only by the tears she shed in private. She sought refuge in the solitude of her room, where the walls were her only confidants. The pain had etched lines of sorrow on her face, transforming her youthful visage into one marked by the weight of her experience.

Anna's existence had become a symphony of muted emotions, a silent lament for the love she had believed in and the life she had lost. Instead of healing, time became a reminder of what was and would never beagain.

During the week, Anna grappled with Nathan'swedding's impending doom, and her heartache reverberated through every moment. Each day felt like an eternity, filled.

With uncertainty and the relentless ache of longing, Anna longed for his presence, an explanation, a signthat their love had not been in vain.

With each passing day, her world grew smaller, closing in around her like the walls of a prison. She haddropped out of school, unable to face her friends andthe life that had so suddenly crumbled. Deception and pride held her captive in a dark cave of despair, whereher smile had become a distant memory, like the faintecho of a melody she could no longer hear.

The outside world continued, but it was like time hadreached a standstill for Anna. Her once-bright dreamshad turned to ash, and the future she had imagined withNathan had disintegrated. The pain etched lines of sorrow on her face, and her hazel eyes, once filled withhope, had dulled to a lifeless gray.

Yet, despite the seemingly endless darkness that had enveloped her, a small glimmer of hope had begun toemerge. A friend's offer to care for a class of kindergartners had brought a flicker of light into herlife. On her first day in the classroom, the presence of these little souls, though intimidating, had opened thedoor to a new world.

The children's innocence, laughter, and boundless joy had worked as a balm for Anna's wounded heart. Eachday, they chipped away at the thick fog of grief.

That had separated her from the outside world. Theveil of shame that had shrouded her slowly dissipated, revealing a glimmer of the woman she used to be.

During the kids' naptime, as the little ones dozed peacefully, Anna found moments of solitude in the classroom. The silence invited her to put her thoughts and emotions into words. She would pull out a notepadand a pen and write letters, not meant to be sent to anyone but as a way to unburden her soul.

She poured her sorrow and pain onto the pages witheach pen stroke. The ink on the paper became a vessel for her unspoken words, grief, and longing. She wrote about the love she had lost, the dreams that had shattered, and the heartache that had consumed her. These letters were her sanctuary, where she could beraw and honest with herself without fear of judgment. The children, unaware of the pain she carried, provideda sense of comfort and healing, and the letters became a bridge between her past and a future yet to be discovered.

As she watched the children learn and grow, she couldn't help but be reminded of the fragility and beauty of life, much like the delicate orchid flowers they tended to. With each interaction, Anna's heart began to mend, and her smile, once lost, returned moregenuine and radiant. Her hazel eyes began to sparkleagain, and the weight that burdened her for so long began to lift. The letters she wrote, though never sent, became a cathartic release, a way to let go of the painand betrayal that had haunted her for years.

Anna's transformation was a testament to the resilience of the human spirit. It was a reminder thateven in the darkest times, there is the potential for healing, growth, and the rediscovery of joy.

CHAPTER IX

FATE' SILENT SYMPHONY

"Destiny, that enigmatic force, weaves the threads of our lives into a mosaic of events beyond our mortal grasp. The cosmic hand guides us, whether in whispered guidance or the weight of inevitability."

Time had proven a steadfast ally to Anna, each passing day gradually aiding in mending wounds inflicted by Nathan's betrayal. The laughter and unquenchable curiosity of the children she cared for had erased the scars etched by a past love gone awry. As a caregiver and educator, she found a renewed sense of purpose in the promise of each day, where fresh beginnings arrived with every new group of young souls she nurtured. It was as though the routine of her life had become a soothing melody, harmonized by the laughter and quirks of the little ones she had come to adore.

Amid her daily routine, Anna was fully immersed in guiding the young ones through their activities. Her heart was aglow with the pure and infectious joy that radiated from their innocent hearts, creating a charming symphony that encapsulated the essence of any typical day at the kindergarten.

Then fate appeared unexpectedly, softly reminding us that the past, however dormant, can stir when we least expect it.

Like a sudden twist orchestrated by the universe, destiny's unforeseen visitor appeared, standing at the threshold. It was Nathan. His arrival felt like an uninvited intrusion, gently unsettling the peace she had painstakingly crafted.

However, he wasn't alone. Clutched in his hand was a toddler's tiny, delicate hand, a living bridge to the shared dreams of their past. The mere sight of him sent a shiver down her spine as if time itself had momentarily folded back, transporting her to a place from which she had fought so hard to move on. In that poignant moment, the lines between the past, present, and the yet-to-be-written future began to blur and sway, unveiling an uncertain canvas ready to be painted.

As their eyes locked in an awkward silence, it was evident that both were overwhelmed by the unexpected reunion. Anna grappled with a whirlwind of emotions, unable to define the precise sentiments coursing through her. Fear was prominent among them as she sensed her heart beating with anxiety, a desperate plea for help echoing within.

Anna gracefully bent down to Freddy's height to make their first meeting more comfortable and steady her quivering knees. She looked at the little boy with a warm smile, her heart a swirl of emotions as she welcomed him, "My name is Anna, and we're going to have a wonderful time together."

Leading him further into the classroom, she gestured for him to follow as she began a cautious tour. She pointed out the various toys and the cozy cushions for their afternoon nap. All the while, Freddy's father, Nathan, stood in a corner of the classroom, watching and observing the surroundings as he closely watched Anna.

Anna couldn't help but notice that Nathan's gaze lingered on her. She saw a flicker of recognition in his eyes, even though it had been years since they had last seen each other. It was evident to her that he still remembered her, and that realization stirred a mix of emotions within her.

Him, for his part, observed Anna's graceful demeanor and the way she interacted with the children. She had not changed a bit, and he couldn't help but marvel at how she had retained her beauty and charm over the years. Anna returned to Nathan as the tour concluded, cradling Freddy in her arms. She requested that Nathan give his son a kiss goodbye as the class was about to begin. She had a friendly, professional demeanor, but her heart was in turmoil beneath it all.

Walking back to her desk, she couldn't help but ponder the incredible coincidence that had brought Nathan and his son to her class. She wondered why her class had been chosen out of all the schools in the city.

Sitting at her desk, she contemplated the situation, her heart in a whirlwind of emotions. Nathan was married now, with a son, yet he remained her Nathan—the man who had once stirred her heart and awakened a flood of feelings she had long tried to bury.

On the days when Nathan dropped off Freddy at the kindergarten, there was a palpable sense of anticipation. Anna and Nathan eagerly looked forward to the moments when their auras would once again merge, greeting each other like long-lost friends. However, the bittersweet farewells at the end of eachday left them with an insatiable craving for the next.

For Anna, each day became a whirlwind of emotions as she teetered between the joy of seeing him and thedread of saying goodbye. Nathan, too, wrestled with his own thoughts, constantly strategizing on how he could invite her for a ride, hoping that it might temper the fiery passion that had reignited within him.

Months passed before Nathan mustered the courage to extend the invitation. One of these days, he approached Anna, his voice trembling with sincerity as he implored, "Please, Anna, grant me the opportunityto clear my conscience and apologize to you. Just once." She hesitated; her heart and mind engaged in afierce internal battle. She fully intended to refuse, butto her own surprise, the word that escaped her lips was,"Okay."

She couldn't believe her own response; she had meant to decline. Yet, her heart again overruled her rationalmind on the agreed-upon Sunday.

He took her to a vineyard away from the city. The sunshine warmed up their fear and dissolved thecoldness of their skin. Her hair followed the wind, gracefully showing the beauty of her naked face. They walked through the vineyard side by side. From time totime, Nathan sneaked a look, absorbing her beauty andhair, which looked like a feather in each blow of thewind. She looked only ahead, silently waiting for hiswords.

As they wandered through the sun-kissed vineyard,Nathan finally found the words he had meant to express. He began, "I know I caused you a lot of pain,"and then he continued, "and I wanted to apologize. Life swept me away from you and set me on a differentpath."

He paused, gathering his thoughts before speaking again, "I don't want to make excuses for my foolish behavior, but I was a man consumed by a big ego andmisguided notions, thinking I could play around withevery girl. I never realized how much I missed you untilI was trapped."

Nathan's voice trembled with a mix of regret and sincerity as he spoke, "My wife deceived me, and I found myself trapped by obligations I couldn't escape. When she became pregnant, the truth came out to both our families, and they insisted we marry immediately. You understand how our village holds fast to tradition." He let out a heavy sigh, his words weighted with remorse. "I'm deeply sorry, and I hope you canfind it in your heart to forgive me. Thoughts of you never left my mind. Despite her being my wife in name,you're the one who holds my heart."

Anna remained silent, her steps carrying her forwardwithout glancing at him. The sweet scent of theripening grapes was like a balm to her soul, and the emerald leaves of the vines urged her to pause and inhale deeply. The lush green surroundings offered asoothing and comforting presence.

Unnoticed by Nathan, a solitary tear traced a glistening path down her cheek. It burned with emotion but seemed to freeze in place. She made no move to wipe it away; what would be the point?

Her voice trembled with a mix of vulnerability andlonging as she turned to face Nathan.

"What do you want from me?" she said. "Do you have any idea how I spent my days and nights? Lovingyou was too hard, and not loving you was harder. I loved you, but was I loved? I wondered, couldn't know.I gave all my hope to you. I broke my pride, which wasunbreakable, and my honor, which I valued greatly. Iwaited every day to see you, waited for you to determine my destiny.

Waiting is hard; being patient is harder. I waited inevery corner of my life for you. My love burned me. Icreated an angel of you and prostrated for her. I gaveall my hope to you."

Nathan listened, his face reflecting the weight of hispast actions, his remorse heavy on his heart. He said,"I just felt a nostalgic longing for the old days. I neededto see you and calm my heart. Please forgive me."

She kept her silence, then asked him to take her back home. The sun dipped lower on the horizon, casting long shadows across the rows of vines. Anna's heartwas heavy with the weight of the encounter, the floodof emotions that had risen within her. She gazed at the serene vineyard, the lush green leaves rustling softly in the breeze.

Nathan, too, was lost in thought. As he drove her back to her home, he couldn't shake the feeling of missed opportunities and lost time. The years had separated them, and their choices had led them on vastly different paths. He realized the depth of his mistakes, not just for leaving her but for how he had left her.

Back at her doorstep, they exchanged no more words. She stepped out of the car, and Nathan watched her as she walked away, her shoulders bearing the invisible weight of their shared history. He understood that forgiveness would be a hard-earned gift, and whether it would ever be granted remained uncertain.

As the car drove away, the quiet of the evening enveloped Anna once more. Her emotions swirled within, a mixture of love, longing, and the pain of their complicated past. The sadness in her eyes persisted, but amid the gloom, there was also a flicker of hope, the faintest glimmer of a future yet to be written.

She couldn't escape the gravitational pull that drew her back into Nathan's orbit. Their encounters multiplied in that secret vineyard, hidden from the world's prying eyes. As the days and nights blended, her heart betrayed her, longing for the man who had once held her so tightly.

In this clandestine realm, the vineyard became their love sanctuary. It was where they wrote a new chapter in their complicated story, where passion flowed like the very wine that surrounded them. The sweet grapes seemed to mirror the sweetness of their forbidden love, and they laughed at the thought of christening a new vintage with a label that read "ECSTASY: Bottled in the highlands of Anna, where Bacchus, the God of wine, himself crafts the elixir."

Their rendezvous was a dance of desire and longing, a fierce embrace that defied the constraints of time and responsibility. In each other's arms, they found refuge from the uncertainties of tomorrow, savoring the ecstasy of their stolen moments.

Her delight was a complex brocade of emotions, a facade of happiness made up of threads of passion and longing. She smiled brightly on the outside, but on the inside, her heart was heavy with guilt. She lived her life as if it were a beautifully wrapped but empty gift, an appearance of joy that masked the darkness within.

The truth loomed over her, casting a shadow on her moments of intimacy with Nathan. She grappled with her own moral compass, struggling to reconcile her actions with her values. How could she be a willing accomplice to Nathan's infidelity? The fear of consequences, of the inevitable reckoning, clawed at the edges of her consciousness.

To allay her anxieties, she blinded herself to the looming repercussions, allowing passion and longing to lead her actions. Her heart clung to the faint hope that this story could end happily. With each passing day, she crossed her fingers and played blind man's buff, chasing elusive happiness through the maze of their forbidden love.

CHAPTER X

FEAR PARADOX

"Fear, when courted, becomes the silent architect ofthe circumstances we wish to avoid."

"Anna's dreamy joy shattered abruptly with the realization of her missing monthly period—a glaringabsence that silently accused her of another foolish andunforgivable act. It was as if the seeds of pleasure sownin that vineyard had not only found fertile ground butalso had, against all odds, blossomed into a new life— a life that felt lost before it even had the chance to trulybegin.

Her world crumbled under the weight of this revelation. She knew with a sinking heart that Nathanwould never leave his wife to marry her. In their small,gossip-ridden village, such a scandal would be an explosive force, forever tarnishing her future. The tongues of the town were sharp and unforgiving, andshe had seen how they could devour a person'sreputation without remorse.

So, as the time for their subsequent encounter in thevineyard neared, it no longer appeared lush and invitingto Anna; instead, it resembled a withered corpse, its vines like brittle, parched bones. The skies above seemed to mirror her turmoil, draped in shades of gray that cloaked her like a heavy, silken shawl meant to smother her shame.

A biting, unrelenting wind blew through her, chillingher to the core, freezing the very essence of her being.She stood on that barren earth, staring into an unknown future, while the relentless wind tossed her hair like a raging sea's wild, tumultuous waves. At thatmoment, it was as if her entire life had been a fragilesandcastle, lovingly built and now ruthlessly dismantledby the powerful force of an angry wave.

When Nathan arrived, it took him no time to sense something was amiss. He drew her into a hug, but thebody he held felt as cold and unmoving as a statue. Hisheart sank, intuition screaming that a storm wasbrewing in her soul. "Anna," he implored, "is there something wrong? Please, tell me." But she remainedeerily silent, her heart's tempest hidden behind a wallof stoic quiet."

As Nathan faced the reality of her pregnancy, his initial shock and discomfort were evident. It was an unexpected situation, and his initial instinct was to turnaway for a moment to collect his thoughts. With a heavy sigh, he turned to face Anna.

The uncomfortable talk continued as Nathanoutlined their limited options, fully aware of thesocietal consequences of an unmarried pregnancy intheir tiny, close-knit community. Her voice, laden withsorrow, agreed that keeping the baby was not a viableoption given their circumstances.

Nathan offered reassurance, promising to provide financial support, though he couldn't change the fundamental reality of their situation. Anna understood the necessity of their decision but couldn't help feeling a profound sense of loss and sadness.

As her pregnancy advanced, she became even more aware of the life growing within her. Her nights were filled with sleepless contemplation, her mind drifting between dreams of the baby she would never hold openly and the questions that swirled within her. What would their child look like? Would they have their father's eyes or her smile? Would the baby be a boy or a girl? These unanswered questions continued to haunt her as she sought to discreet solution for the impending challenges ahead.

Her situation weighed heavily on me, and I couldn't help but worry about her well-being. She could not easily share her predicament with the townsfolk, as the judgment and condemnation they would inevitably face in their small, close-knit community were unbearable. She was a young girl, only twenty years old, facing the daunting prospect of an unplanned pregnancy, and I knew she needed support and guidance.

I did my best to discreetly assist her in seeking medical help. Finding a doctor who could provide the necessary care and discretion was challenging in a town where everyone seemed to know everyone else's business. I couldn't bear to see Anna's sleepless nights spent worrying, knowing that her situation was not her own choosing and that she was building a dream that would remain unfulfilled.

As her pregnancy advanced, my concerns for her grew. I wanted to be there for her, to help her find thebest possible solution, and to provide comfort in hertime of need.

She had to navigate a difficult path, and I wished tostand beside her as a friend and a source of support throughout her journey.

Anna's despair seemed impossible, and I could do little more than offer my silent presence and support.The weight of guilt pressed heavily upon her heart, andshe blamed herself for falling into Nathan's trap for thesecond time. Her situation was nothing short of a heart-wrenching ordeal.

After a night of restless contemplation, Anna decided to confide in her older, married sister. She implored hersister for assistance, and her sister, understanding the dire circumstances, agreed to help. At first, they tried herbal remedies, but they proved ineffective, leavingAnna's agony to grow with each passing day. She grappled with the profound guilt of seeking to terminate an innocent life, wondering if her financialsituation had been better; perhaps she could have pursued a different path. But life's complexities are rarely as accommodating as our desires.

Her sister eventually located a clandestine clinic for an abortion, and their shared journey took them to a dubious neighborhood. The clinic's yard, enclosed by barren fruit trees, cast a chilling shadow over the grim occasion. These fruit trees, with their sickly, green appearance, seemed to mirror the desolation thatpervaded our hearts that day. Just like the unfortunate fetuses that were to be removed, these fruits never reached their full ripeness. Instead, they hung from the branches, shriveled and unfulfilled, echoing the eerie sense of incompleteness that loomed in the air.

The day we arrived at the clinic, the sun shone brightly overhead, enveloping Anna in its warmth. Her determination was her armor as we parked close to the front door, both of us apprehensively knocking on its surface. Fear and anxiety left us both silent, trapped in the numbing embrace of uncertainty and dread.

After waiting for what felt like an eternity in the dimly lit waiting room, I observed the stale, pale green walls adorned with old posters about women's health. The air was thick with anxiety, and the quiet hum of a flickering fluorescent light above was the only sound that dared to intrude upon the eerie silence.

In contrast to the oppressive atmosphere, the man who led us through this uncomfortable journey seemed oddly composed. His clinical attire was crisp and sterile, a stark contrast to the emotional turmoil that surrounded us. The lines on his face spoke of years of experience, an unsettling reminder of the clandestine nature of his work.

As she disappeared into the other room, I strained to hear any hint of her discomfort or distress, but the walls seemed to absorb every sound. All that remained was the haunting silence, amplifying our shared trepidation. It was as if we had stepped into a world that thrived on secrecy and shadows, far removed from the safe haven of familiar healthcare facilities.

In the waiting area, I sat in silence, my anxiety mounting with each passing minute. Time seemed to stretch endlessly, amplifying the unsettling clinic atmosphere. The air was thick with apprehension, and the quiet magnified every sound.

Hearing Anna's muffled screams left me seething with anger—a wave of anger directed at Nathan for his betrayal, the narrow-minded townsfolk, and even Anna herself. I couldn't help but think of the promises I'd made to myself never to find myself entangled in such a situation, and my heart ached for my friend.

After an agonizing twenty minutes, the doctor emerged from the room and approached me. His words were delivered with a cold detachment that sent shivers down my spine. "All is done," he declared, then added the crushing blow, "She can never have kids again." My heart broke anew as I contemplated the irreversible consequences of this procedure for my dear friend.

Anna, on the other hand, despite her relatively young age, had little concern for her future fertility. All she yearned for was to escape her stifling hometown and embark on a new chapter in her life. The very thought of Nathan with him sent shivers of dread down her spine, and he, in turn, acted as if the guilt of his actions had transformed him into a frightened, tail-tucked dog.

In the wake of the procedure, she decided to call the school and request her release from her position. She knew that her fragile heart could not withstand the continued presence of Freddy and his father, a daily reminder of a life she desperately wished to leave behind. In time, she learned that Freddy, too, had left the school.

For a couple of weeks, she cocooned herself within the confines of her home, her once-vibrant spirit now numbed by her ordeal. Her only connection to the outside world was the window that faced the Blueberry tree and the quiet street. Her vacant gaze lingered on the world outside, but it saw nothing, thought of nothing, and dreamt of nothing. Amid this desolation, there was one thing that continued to remind her of her existence—the relentless, painful bleeding that served as a stark and constant reminder of the cruelty and ugliness of the world she inhabited.

CHAPTER XI

ANNA

Anna resumed attending church during the week instead of the usual Sunday service. It was a simple yetprofound act that helped her find solace amid the chaos of her life. Each visit to the hallowed space offered her a heavenly respite from the weight of herpast.

In the quiet church, she would sit alone, her heartlaid bare before her faith. Her prayers and meditations were sincere, filled with pleas for guidance and forgiveness. It was here that she sought strength to heal, a path toward redemption, and a way to cleanseher soul.

Her physical transformation, evident in her shrinking figure, became increasingly concerning to her family, especially her mother and sister. They watched as thelight in Anna's eyes dimmed, replaced by shadows of her suffering. Desperate to help her find peace and renewal, they decided on a plan.

The decision was to send Anna to the city, where she could stay with a trusted friend for a couple of months. It was a hopeful opportunity for her to leave behind the painful memories that clung to her small town like a ghost. The prospect of the city offered a glimmer of hope, though Anna's heart felt heavy with uncertainty.

On the day of her departure, her sister brought her to a bustling taxi lot. It was a day devoid of excitement or anticipation; instead, it felt like the closing of a chapter. I held Anna close, kissed her on both cheeks, and whispered words of encouragement.

"My dear Anna, trust in God," I said. "Better days will arrive, and you will find your way back to happiness. In the metropolis, find solace in the possibilities of the future, because what lays behind you should not be forgotten. You are a young, beautiful soul, and this incident should not determine your destiny. Nurture your spirit with hope and knowledge, and may God bless you. "Go find the peace you deserve."

"Friendship, like gems in life's mosaic, shines through loyal hearts that uplift you in the darkest hours, steer you clear of missteps, and craft bonds thatstand the test of time. While others may falter, these enduring connections are the true treasures."

In the twilight of life, nostalgia takes hold. We sit down, sipping the bittersweet wine of reflection, andcarefully comb through the tapestry of days gone by.The recollections of sun-kissed moments and laughter become treasures we hold dear, while the somber shadows of difficult times morph into distant wisps of memory, fading like a smoky, far-off dream.

As we move through different stages of life, we come to appreciate its complex tapestry. Our experiences area mix of joy, victory, sadness, and loss. We all have apart to play in this drama, leaving our mark on the stageof life. Each action we take is recognized in its own way, whether through celebration or devotion. As thefinal curtain falls, we retreat behind the scenes, readyfor the encore that lies ahead in the pages of our unwritten screenplay.

Thinking back on my memories, I am reminded of adear friend named Fadia. Her name alone evokes a sense of nostalgia and a rush of emotions. She was anexceptional soul, and our shared narrative is a treasuredchapter in my life.

One particular day comes to mind. It was a summer morning, with the sun illuminating the sky, when mymother invited me to accompany her on her customary visits to our neighbors. The countryside stretched outbefore us, a stunning scene of vivid, flowering gardens and fresh flowers floating through the warm air. Thepleasant breeze rustled the leaves of the nearby trees,and birds decorated the sky with joyous sounds. It wasa scene of calm and tenderness, the ideal setting for theday that would etch Fadia's memories even more deeply into my heart.

When I asked my mother why she wanted me to come with her, she simply said she wanted my company. Since it was a school holiday and I had no set plans, I welcomed the moment's spontaneity. I quickly freshened up and we were off. The morning was definitely different. The sun's golden rays wrappedeverything in a warm embrace, and a sense of adventure persisted in the air. Our separate homes, which had innumerable stories and mysteries, were only a few minutes' walk apart. We walked along theunpaved, lovely street, a symphony of solitude interrupted only by the melodious notes of singing birds and the sudden crowing of a rooster, sending animportant message that only we could comprehend.

Our community emanated a peaceful beauty, bathedin the sun's warm embrace. It was a beautiful paradise,surrounded by soft sloping hills and fields that went as far as the eye could see. Our charming cottages createda harmonic ensemble, their terracotta roofs blendingeffortlessly with the thick vegetation that surrounded us. Life here was basic, and our summer vacations werefrequently filled with simple joys. We spent our timedoing housework, learning about the culinary arts, listening to music, or letting our creative energies runwild.

For me, those sun-kissed days were synonymous withpainting and crafting. The act of creating art with myown hands was my true calling. I embarked on a mission to replicate the enigmatic Mona Lisa, a task Iapproached with equal parts enthusiasm and determination. My attempts were numerous, and I lost count of how many iterations I created. At times, hereyes would come to life and bear an uncanny resemblance to one of my school friends. In other attempts, I inadvertently bestowed her with petite, angry eyes, starkly contrasting the original's sweet andenigmatic gaze. Despite my tenacity, I eventually surrendered to the complexities of the Mona Lisa and transitioned to a more forgiving canvas—cartoon characters. Their simplicity offered a refreshing change, and I reveled in the delightful ease with which they allowed my creativity to flow.

As we walked along the path to our neighbor's house, I couldn't resist inquiring again about my mother's unusual invitation. "Why did you ask me to come along today?" I questioned. She responded, "I thought it would be a good opportunity for you to have some company during your vacation. You tend to be on yourown a lot. Plus, she's your age, a lovely girl." "Okay," Iagreed, though I couldn't shake the niggling doubt thatsomething more lay behind this invitation.

Before I introduce you to Fadia, let me immerse youin the rich folk tale of our village's customs.

In the heart of our village, a cherished tradition among the women unfolded with the rising sun. Likeclockwork, they embarked on early morning visits, their footsteps echoing through the cobblestone streets at around 6 or 7 AM. These visits were not mere socialcalls but a ritual that bound our community together.

As they gathered, the women would partake in the pleasure of sipping freshly brewed Turkish coffee. With each delicate sip, they engaged in spirited chatter,reveled in the art of gossip, and shared the latest chapters of their lives, punctuated by the timeless chorus of complaints. The aroma of freshly ground coffee beans mingled with the warmth of camaraderie.

But the true magic happened once the last drops ofcoffee had been savored. The emptied cups, now imbued with stories and secrets, underwent a transformation. With a graceful swirl and a flick of the wrist, each cup was upended onto its saucer, the grounds forming a mosaic of destiny. This intricate mosaic held within it a world of symbols and secrets,each a key to unlocking the enigmatic path that lay ahead.

It was these symbols that stoked the fires of anticipation, especially among us, the young andhopeful. We yearned to glimpse the unknown future, our hearts echoing with the question: Would weencounter our prince? When and where would our destinies intertwine, and what form would he take?

For the older women, the stakes were often higher, their thrills tinged with concerns of financial fortune or husbands' fidelity. These morning gatherings were nothing short of a sacred rite, a timeless tapestry of connection and revelation. The stories and prophecies spun within these walls often stretched the bounds of time, sometimes extending these visits for hours on end.

CHAPTER XII

TIMELESS CUSTOMS

"Customs are the unspoken norms that influencesociety, combining old practices with new ones, andkeeping cultures rooted in the past of time."

Like many in our Middle Eastern village, Fadia's house carried a unique charm. Its stone walls held stories of generations past, and the windows adornedwith blue wooden trim exuded a rustic elegance. Theweathered door, marked with countless scratches likethe healing scars of a wound, hinted at years of welcoming visitors.

As we stood on the stone front step, worn smooth and shiny by the passage of countless footsteps, I couldn't help but feel a sense of timelessness. The stone beneath my feet seemed to whisper tales of laughter, shared moments, and the ebb and flow of life in our close-knit community.

When our knock echoed through the weathered door, a girl around my age welcomed us inside. Her long, jet-black hair cascaded down her back, framing captivating, coal-black eyes. Her thick, arching eyebrows gave her a determined, slightly mysterious look as if she carried secrets.

Fadia's mother kindly asked her daughter to prepare the coffee, and my own mother requested that I assist. Together, we made our way to the kitchen, where the fragrant aroma of brewing coffee filled the air. In this cozy setting, I took a moment to introduce myself to Fadia, and we set about arranging the coffee cups on a tray. Fadia skillfully prepared traditional Turkish coffee, expertly combining finely ground coffee beans with water and a touch of sugar called "Ahwe wassat." The mixture simmered, gradually forming a frothy, inviting brew that promised warmth and companionship in each cup.

In the blink of an eye, Fadia and I formed a bond that seemed to defy time. Our friendship blossomed as quickly as the flowers in our gardens. We would often escape the confines of our homes to explore the wild beauty of the bushes surrounding our houses. Those long walks were filled with chatter and laughter; during these moments, we optimal grazing areas but our adventures didn't end with walks in the wilderness. Fadia and I were eager to learn new things together. We took up card games, mastering the intricacies of the rules and competing with the fierce determination of champions. We even embarked on the art of knitting, needles clicking in harmony as we crafted scarves and blankets while sharing stories and dreams.

In the enchanting realm of coffee cup reading, Fadia's mother introduced us to a mystical art that quickly stole our hearts. It was a world where the remnants of our coffee cups held secrets and stories waiting to be deciphered, where intricate patterns and symbols spokevolumes about the past, present, and future.

With each session, our fascination grew, drawing us deeper into the captivating allure of this ancientpractice. I found myself consumed by a relentless curiosity, eager to uncover the origins of coffee cup reading and unravel the mysteries hidden within its symbols.

Guided by Fadia's mother and other seasoned interpreters, I delved into the rich tapestry of symbolism, meticulously studying each symbol and itssignificance. Hours were spent poring over texts, absorbing knowledge, and honing my skills in the artof interpretation.

Practicing on Fadia and others became more than amere hobby; it became a passionate pursuit, a journeyof discovery and self-discovery. In those moments ofdivination through coffee grounds, I felt a profound connection to something greater than myself, a timeless tradition that transcended cultures and centuries.

COFFEE'S ORIGIN

Here is what I found out about the origin of coffee beans and the reading.

The story begins with Kaldi, a young goatherd who lived in the verdant Ethiopian highlands. His unwavering commitment to caring for his goat herd earned him widespread renown in the village. He would guide them daily as they traversed the hills, seeking optimal grazing areas.

As Kaldi pushed himself farther into the hills than normal on a bright morning, he made an unusual observation. Amidst the verdant foliage, he noticed unusual, bright red berries. Curious, he picked a handful of berries and put them in his mouth. Something extraordinary occurred the second the sour and bitter taste reached his tongue. A refreshing surge of energy coursed through Kaldi's body, causing his once drooping eyelids to fly open and his perceptions to sharpen.

Because the berries had such a profound impact on him, Kaldi couldn't help but tell everyone about them. He returned to the village in a flash, ready to share the news of these miraculous berries with everyone. One of the village men was a revered scholar who paid close attention while Kaldi told her tale. He decided to give the berries a go because he was curious about the goatherd's renewed energy.

He couldn't believe it, but the berries were just as energizing. Realizing the potential of these crimson marvels filled him with excitement. Returning to the village with Kaldi, he continued to gather berries.

They went back to the village and started playing with this strange fruit. They gave them a go uncooked, but the bitter flavorturned them off. Unfazed, the scholar conceived of a plan. Heroasted the beans over an open fire with the berries, and as they cooked, a wonderful aroma wafted through the air, like the most heavenly fragrance you've ever smelled.

It was a mind-blowing change. Pulverized into a fine powder, the now-brown and aromatic roasted beans were steeped in a dark, invigorating elixir. Feeling revitalized and full of life, the peasants rejoiced as they sipped the hot drink. It was as if thegods had showered them with a holy elixir, a gift from above.

Going to faraway countries, nearby cities, and even remote mountain monasteries didn't take long. As its name was eventually known, coffee was no longer a closely guarded secret buta beloved discovery everyone could enjoy.

Over the years that followed, coffee spread to all parts of the world, where diverse cultures brought their own special ways of making and enjoying this mystical beverage. A new social and intellectual scene emerged as coffeehouses mushroomed.

However, coffee's journey continued beyond that point. Readingcoffee grounds became a popular technique in subsequent years, drawing inspiration from the ancient Chinese habit of reading tealeaves. Many would look into their coffee cups, hoping to find answers to life's mysteries or glimpse the future through the patterns and symbols left behind.

But there were challenges along the way for coffee. The Sultan of the Ottoman Empire outlawed coffee in the name of Islamiclaw because of its narcotic status and the belief that it had sexualproperties. Still, the devotion to coffee was unwavering, even when prohibition existed. Its persistence was guaranteed by itssmuggling via noisy marketplaces and crowded bazaars.

Before Sultan Suleiman the Magnificent' s rule, coffee didn't formally gain popularity in Turkey and other countries until the 16th century. Coffeehouses saw explosive growth, transforming into lively cultural, discourse, and amusement hubs.

So began the epic voyage of coffee, which began in the Ethiopian highlands and ended in the hearts of innumerable civilizations worldwide. It was a gift from the gods that transformed people, brought them together in homes and cafes, and fostered conversations and friendships for generations. Awakening and sharing delight have always been essential themes in the coffee story.

My reputation as a coffee cup reader spread throughout the neighborhood as my skills honed. The word of my talent reached the ears of other girls ourage, and soon, we were hosting afternoon gatherings filled with excitement and anticipation. We'd huddle together, cups in hand, as I guided them through the mesmerizing journey of coffee cup reading.

Laughter and camaraderie filled those gatherings, and although not every reading revealed life-altering secrets, we cherished the shared experience. We celebrated moments of insight and wisdom, and eventhe occasional disappointments became sources of amusement. Our friendship grew stronger with each cup we read and each secret we unveiled.

In the warm afternoons of our youth, surrounded by the enchanting world of coffee cup readings, Fadia andI forged a bond that transcended time and left an indelible mark on our hearts. With our newfound friends, we embarked on a magical journey, finding joy in the mysteries of the future and the pleasures of thepresent.

It was a tranquil afternoon at my house, the goldensunlight streaming through the windows, casting warmpatterns on the table where Fadia and I sat. Our friendship had blossomed into something beautiful and unique, and we cherished the moments we spent together, seeking adventure in the ordinary.

On this particular day, we decided to indulge in oneof our favorite pastimes: coffee cup reading. The aroma of freshly brewed coffee wafted through the room as Fadia handed me her cup, her eyes shimmering with excitement. Little did we know thatthe patterns and symbols nestled in the dark liquid would soon set in motion a series of events that would change our lives in ways we couldn't have imagined.

As I gazed into the depths of Fadia's coffee cup, I wasgreeted by an unexpected sight. The swirling coffee grounds seemed to merge into a mesmerizing tableauof symbols. A man stood tall and mysterious, his silhouette framed by the comforting shade of a tree. On the other side of the cup, two swans glided gracefully, their presence serene and captivating. An upside-down cross etched itself onto the opposite side, its meaning shrouded in enigma. And at the bottom of the cup, a sea of darkness loomed, a symbol ofprofound love, yet one fraught with trials and tears.

At that moment, the air was thick with a sense of theuncanny, but we couldn't help but chuckle and dismiss it as a lighthearted game. We spun whimsical tales based on the symbols we had just uncovered, relishing the imaginative stories we concocted.

Little did we know that the laughter that echoed through my house that day would soon give way to astonishment as the predictions hidden within the coffee cup reading began to materialize before our eyes. Our lives were poised on the precipice of a dramatic transformation, and the coffee cup had unknowingly offered us a glimpse into the tapestry of fate. The playful afternoon we had shared was about to unravel into a story of profound significance, forever altering the course of our destinies.

CHAPTER XIII
DEBATING DESTINY

In our world, the question of destiny divides beliefinto two camps: some say our choices determine it, while others believe it's written in the stars. Even experts like coffee cup readers can't unravel its mystery.

Destiny's unpredictable nature adds to the intrigue.We use cards, mediums, and zodiac cups to decipher it,yet it remains elusive, almost as if it resists ourunderstanding.

Fate, however, offers an alternative. It's the force thatguides our hearts, often leading us down unexpectedpaths. We all experience it in some form, nudging ustowards significant choices and experiences.

Fadia's life is a testament to the interplay between destiny, choices, and the enigmatic role of fate. Whether destiny is a result of our choices or cosmic patterns, and whether fate gently guides us or remainsunseen, one thing is clear: life's mysteries are profoundand shape our unique journey in the grand tapestry ofexistence.

On a splendid morning, a whimsical sense of adventure danced through the hearts of my two school friends and me. We formed a trio of intrepid explorers, drawn irresistibly by the promise of discovery, casting our gaze upon the enchanting Wadi el Aarayesh, lovingly known as the "grapevine valley." This idyllic locale held an extra layer of charm, for it was home toZahle's famed open-air restaurants, each a treasure waiting to be unveiled.

With July's sun already stretching its warm fingers across the horizon, we were determined to seize the day before the unforgiving heat set in. As the morning sun painted the world with its golden hues, we forgedan unwavering pact to gather at 8 AM, right by at thatappointed hour, we converged upon our meeting place,our hearts dancing with anticipation. We were a trio of kindred spirits, all brimming with excitement at the Kadri Hotel.

KADRI HOTEL

This charming institution was owned by the parentsof one of our dear friend, adding to the charm of ourmeeting.

We felt excited at every step, giving our adventure a charming edge. The day was prepared for suspense andwonder as we searched Wadi el Aarayesh for hiddengems.

Imagine entering a world where history permeates every corner and time has left its mark. The majesticfacade of The Kadri Hotel, built in 1906, echoed the stories it would witness.

War ravaged the neighborhood in 1914, and the Turkish army ruled the hotel. As a hospital during World War I, its exquisite rooms became a bustling headquarters and refuge.

However, a fateful 1920 day would immortalize The Hotel. The French Mandate authorities declared the judiciary's annexation within these sacred walls. This statement established "Greater Lebanon," as we know it.

The Hotel's history is still felt when you enter. Woodand steel doors welcome you with their grandeur. Time-polished bronze knobs shine like gems. Your feetwill walk on an uneven stone-paved floor that has seenmany footsteps over the years.

But the large balcony with its front-row view of thebusy main street steals the show. Towering trees provide privacy for the hotel's prominent guests withtheir huge canopy. Each room and corridor of The Kadri Hotel tells a narrative of the past. Time has leftan indelible mark, as the present and past dance in aneternal waltz.

Beneath the welcoming shade of the hotel's balcony, a wave of euphoria swept over us, carrying our voicesto heights of giddy exhilaration. Our laughter and chatter filled the air, a testament to the pure joy of ourimpending adventure. But the gracious hospitality ofher parents soon intervened, silencing our exuberance for the comfort of their esteemed guest.

And what a day it was! Bathed in the sun's warm embrace, we embarked on our girls' day out, a journey bound by the threads of friendship and the promise ofnew experiences. The world was ours to explore, andtogether, we created memories that would forever bindour hearts.

CHAPTER XIV

FADIA

"Life Unfolds in a Series of Surprises: The Dance of the Known and Unknown."

Those were the good old days when our worries wereas light as the pages of our textbooks. Life was an openbook filled with bright expectations, each promising a better tomorrow. We were young, innocent, and perhaps a tad naive. Back then, the idea that our dreamscould one day be shrouded in deception never crossed our minds.

As I've journeyed through the years, I've come to understand that life unfolds in a series of surprises. Each revelation reveals its own layer of truth, like peeling back the pages of a captivating story. It's as ifone discovery leads to another, creating an intricate web of wonder and intrigue.

In this grand tapestry of existence, secrets unravel before our eyes, yet there always seems to be another layer of profound complexity beyond our grasp. Wecan never truly predict what new surprises will unfold in our lives. From one revelation, we learn that moreawait, bringing both joys and sorrows. Life's currents flow like alternating waves, offering moments of happiness while sometimes sweeping away the things that once brought us joy.

It's the eternal dance of the known and the unknown that weaves the rich fabric of our existence, serving as a reminder that life's most beautiful and poignant moments often emerge from the depths of its captivating nature.

Around noon, we found our haven beneath the generous canopy of a towering tree, its leaves adorned in a lush shade of paradise green. Despite the uneven ground beneath us, we unpacked our provisions with anxious hands and laid a cozy blanket. Nature's grandeur stretched before our eyes, offering a sumptuous feast for our senses.

Above us, the leaves rustled harmoniously, whispering, resembling the gentle bubbling of a frozen, enchanted soup. Sunlight, filtered through the dense foliage, descended in golden shafts as if orchestrating a grand play and spotlighting each of our faces. We basked in this natural stage, feeling like the honored performers in a drama written by our universe.

In our country, the tradition of outdoor picnics was a cherished affair, and we were far from alone in celebrating nature's bounty. In various spots around us, groups had gathered, each with their own assortment of delectable dishes, musical instruments, and hookahs in tow. The air hummed with excitement and camaraderie, a symphony of laughter and music.

The tantalizing aroma of burning charcoal began to waltz through the air as the day progressed. Groups nearby embarked on their culinary adventures, sizzling and grilling an array of delicious foods. The scent mingled with the earthy aroma of the lush surroundings, creating an intoxicating bouquet that enveloped us, making the experience a true feast for the senses.

Ah, the captivating scent of burning charcoal, a culinary pleasure that has always warmed my heart. It has a certain magic, infusing food with an alluring aroma that awakens the senses and stirs our anticipation. The gentle sizzle and crackle of the grill create a delightful intro, setting the stage for the flavors to come.

But for us, our picnic took on a simpler, more rustic charm. Our menu featured tabbouleh, a delightful medley of fresh herbs and bulgur, and hard-boiled eggs and mashed potatoes. These unpretentious dishes were transformed by a drizzle of olive oil, a sprinkle of salt, and a dash of ground black pepper. There was no grilling, no savory scents to tempt our taste buds.

Yet, our picnic was a celebration of simplicity, a reminder that even the most humble ingredients can bring joy when shared in the great outdoors. While we may not have indulged in the smoky allure of grilled fare, the flavors of our meal were a testament to the pleasure of togetherness in nature's embrace.

Right across from our chosen picnic spot was a gathering of about nine individuals—a merry mix of lively young men and women. Their grill, the epicenter of gastronomic delight, belched forth smoke signals that carried with them the tantalizing aroma of kebabs in the making. It was as if the universe had conspiredto turn our senses into eager food detectives, hot on the flavor trail.

Now, picture this: their blanket was like a treasure map, dotted with appetizers that practically begged for attention, fresh bread as soft as clouds, bottles of arak that winked playfully in the sunlight, and those kebabs—sizzling away with a charisma that could rivala celebrity chef. Every skewer had a story to tell, and they whispered promises of mouthwatering adventures.

Their laughter and witty banter filled the air with an infectious energy, like a live comedy show spilling overinto the great outdoors. And us? Well, we couldn't helpourselves. We gazed upon their banquet with all the subtlety of treasure hunters trying to score the ultimate culinary jackpot. We must have looked like a bunch of hungry cats, eyes wide with longing, paws twitching in anticipation, and a collective hope that a morsel of theirdelicious spread might find its way to us, the ultimatefood aficionados!

On that unforgettable day, a man held court over thegrill— an impressive figure, tall and lean with an athlete's physique, Fadia. He seemed to share a magnetic connection, their eyes locking in a silent understanding. As the enchanting aroma of the barbecue enveloped us, it was as if we were all under a spell, unable to tear our eyes away from the sizzling spectacle. Our noses strained towards the mouthwatering fragrance, and I wouldn't be surprised if our stomachs started singing in harmony.

The vigilant grill master had noticed us and perhapseven overheard our lighthearted remarks. Later, the griller strolled confidently in our direction, introducinghimself as Tarek with a friendly smile. He extended apolite invitation for us to join his group. While it was a courteous offer, accepting immediately felt a bit awkward. After all, mere introductions don't instantly forge friendships.

On the other hand, Fadia seemed eager to embrace the invitation and might have done so if not for the cautious glances the rest of us exchanged. Our expressions conveyed a mix of curiosity and uncertainty, creating a moment of hesitation andcontemplation.

Tarek's initial invitation to join their group for a gameof hide-and-seek felt like a warm and welcoming embrace. The offer introduced us to a newfound circle of friends and enveloped us in a cozy sense of curiosityand anticipation.

As he called us to partake in the upcoming game, itwas as if he had extended a hand, inviting us to step out of our comfort zones and bask in the comforting glow of spontaneity. The air was thick withcamaraderie, and the excitement of the unknown flowed warmly through our blood. Eagerly, we presented ourselves, our expressions a blend of enthusiasm and anticipation, not entirely sure of the delightful surprises that awaited.

Playing hide-and-seek with this recently established group was like entering a haven of connection and shared adventures. It was a meaningful gesture beyondsimple play; it was an opportunity to establish relationships and discover one another's strengths and vulnerabilities, all wrapped in the loving embrace of thenatural surroundings.

As we immersed ourselves in the game, seamlesslymelding with the trees and bushes, we couldn't help butfeel the cozy, magnetic pull of the moment. Tarek's invitation had set the stage for an experience beyondthe confines of a simple game; it was about nurturing new connections, embarking on uncharted journeys, and, perhaps, finding a warmth and kinship thatextended well beyond the joy of the game itself.

As we dispersed into the natural surroundings, the verdant foliage became our camouflage. The bush enveloped us like a comforting embrace, its leaves rustling gently as we hid among them. Laughter and hushed whispers filled the air, creating an atmosphere of playful secrecy.

The game itself was a fusion of strategy and spontaneity. We sought the perfect hiding spots, strategically positioning ourselves behind trees and amidst thickets, our hearts beating in rhythm with theanticipation of being found. Tarek, with his infectious enthusiasm, led the group with flair. His laughter echoed through the trees as he counted to start the search, his eyes twinkling mischievously.

As the seekers roamed the bush in search of hidden treasures—us—we observed their movements with bated breath. The thrill of evasion was intoxicating, and every rustle of leaves or the snap of a twig beneath a careless footstep sent a wave of excitement through us.

Moments of connection and bonding emerged amidst the game. Whispered secrets were exchanged, alliances formed, and occasionally, someone would accidentally give away their position with a muffled giggle. It was a game that brought us closer together, a shared experience transcending the simple act of seeking and hiding.

The game drew to a close as the sun dipped below the horizon, casting a warm, golden glow over the bush. We emerged from our leafy hideaways, faces flushed with the thrill of the chase and the joy of newfound friendships. The bush had become more than just a backdrop; it had been the setting for an unforgettable adventure that had woven us all closer together.

As the clock neared 3:30, we reluctantly decided to pack up and bid farewell to our newfound friends. We had spent a glorious day immersed in the beauty of the landscape, filled with laughter and moments of connection.

With a sense of contentment and peacefulness, we expressed our gratitude to Tarek and the others for our wonderful time.

However, as we were about to depart, Tarek approached Fadia with a subtle, knowing smile. He handed her a small piece of paper, a folded note with a mystery within its confines. Their eyes locked for a moment, an unspoken understanding passing between them, and then he simply walked away, leaving Fadia holding the note.

As we drove away from that beautiful landscape, the car had an air of curiosity and intrigue. Fadia carefully unfolded the note, and her eyes scanned the handwritten words. What secrets or messages did it hold? The day may have ended, but it seemed that a new chapter was just beginning, and the note from Tarek was the first page of this intriguing story.

CHAPTER XV

INTUITION LOVE

"First sight love: where intuition speaks louder thanlogic, and the heart knows before the mind comprehends."

Was it love at first sight? Or is that just a fairy tale? Some swear by it, saying love can strike like lightning,an electric spark that defies explanation. It could be Cupid's arrow, fate, or a connection from past lives.

But real love, the kind that goes soul-deep, is morethan what meets the eye. It's a connection that transcends words and gestures, where a single look orword says everything. You know you've found it wheneven a simple touch stirs emotions.

What's more beautiful than that unspoken understanding, that silent language that flows heart toheart? There's nothing quite like that instant soul connection.

The week following the enchanting picnic it promised excitement and anticipation for Fadia. With eachpassing day, she counted down to Sunday with excitement and anxiousness that kept her on her toes.

She had a plan in mind and asked me to accompany her, enlisting me as a willing accomplice to her secret rendezvous.

Their Rendezvous was programmed to take place in the tranquil park of Men Shieh, conveniently close to my friend's parents' hotel, The Hotel Kadri. This time, there was no need for the long hike through the picturesque landscape, making their meeting even more enticing.

Fadia and Tarek's encounters became more frequent as the days turned into weeks. Her euphoria knew no bounds, and her affection for him deepened with each stolen moment they shared. Gradually, Tarek inched closer to our village, drawn by the magnetic pull of their love. It was a clandestine affair, hidden from prying eyes, a secret love blossoming in the shadows. Even as winter descended with its biting cold, their love refused to be extinguished. If anything, their passion burned hotter than ever. They became inseparable, unable to bear being apart for even a single day. The chill in the air did nothing to cool the flames of their love; it only intensified their desire to be with each other, no matter the obstacles in their path.

If only they had glimpsed the future's surprises!

CHAPTER XVI

TIMELESS WHISPERS

"Akachic Records: Where every note whispers a story, and every beat echoes a journey through time."

"My window, my Akashic record, my book of life," I write these words as I sit before the glass pane thathas witnessed the unfolding of my existence. This window, through which I peer into the world, serves asa canvas for the stories of my life. With every gaze, I inscribe another page of my personal narrative, painting the chapters of my journey one view at a time.

Observing raindrops tracing their delicate paths on my window's glass, I couldn't help but be reminded of Fadia's tears, which had fallen like gentle drops later coursing down her cheeks. With a tender gesture, I extended my hand to the glass as if I could wipe away her tears once more, just as I had done when her heart was heavy with sorrow.

I could feel the warmth of the raindrops against the cold surface, and with each crash and boom of the thunderstorm's echoes, I was transported back to the haunting memory of her screams of agony. I recalled how she had called out to Allah, seeking His help and compassion during those moments of profound despair. The sweet love that once filled our hearts with joy and happiness had transformed into a painful sadness, a deep longing, and a loss that echoed in the thunder's roar.

One memory that remains etched in my mind is how her eyes beseeched me, filled with questions that yearned for answers to the enigma of her tragic love story. She gazed at me as though I held the solution, as if I were her savior. But, All I could offer was my attentive silence in those moments, for I possessed no magical answers. My role was simply to hold her close, to shield her fragile heart.

It was her tragic love story, a stark reminder of the undeniable truth that Tarek was a Muslim while she was not. The complexities of their diverse backgrounds and the weight of their families' expectations cast a long, dark shadow over the love they shared.

Seeking clarity, I asked, my voice tinged with urgency,

"How did your parents come to know of your secret?"

She sighed heavily, her voice trembling as shecontinued, "I cannot say for certain, but I suspect someone from our neighborhood must have witnessed our clandestine meetings and reported them to my parents. Their fury was boundless upon discovery, and they issued a dire ultimatum: end the love or be sent away." The pain and despair in her voice were palpable,a testament to the depth of her love for him and the looming tragedy that threatened to engulf them both.

Tears welled up in her eyes, glistening like precious gems of sadness. Her love for him was an all- consuming fire that had burned brightly in her heart,and now, it faced the chilling winds of separation. Itwas as if the essence of Fadia's being was entwined with Tarek's, and the thought of losing him tore at hersoul.

She wiped away a tear with a trembling hand, her voice choked with the intensity of her emotions. "I don't know how we can go on like this, but I can't bearthe thought of losing Tarek," she whispered, her wordscarrying the weight of a love so profound that it defied the boundaries set by the world around them.

Fadia had made a solemn promise that weighed heavily on her heart. She had pledged to end the passionate romance that had blossomed between them. Despite the undeniable intensity of their connection,she affirmed that he was merely a temporary diversion during her otherwise dull summer. She declared her readiness to return to her studies, a decision that carried a heavy sense of tragedy. It was a heart- wrenching reality they both had to face: he was Muslim,and they could not be together. The simplicity of that truth was as painful as it was undeniable.

Her parents, fully aware of the situation, spared noeffort to enforce their wishes. Their solution was to confine her within the four walls of their home,imprisoning her both physically and emotionally. Fadia's heart ached, and her days were spent by the window, gazing out into the world beyond. As her friend, I occasionally check on her, harboring a flicker of hope that she might ask me to read her coffee cup.I longed for a glimmer of optimism, a sign of a new direction in her life.

I can still vividly recall the memory of her wide, imploring black eyes as they locked onto mine, silentlyseeking me for a glimpse into her future.

Unfortunately, I had no hopeful predictions to offer. I yearned to see anything, even though I had resolvednot to vocalize any fabricated visions. I didn't want Fadia to become dependent on imagined words and prophecies, knowing that the only truth she needed toconfront was the painful reality of the present moment.

A few weeks later, I was on my way home from a localmarket when I unexpectedly encountered Tarek standing before me. The moment our eyes met, a sparkof longing ignited in his gaze, and he couldn't help but inquire about her.

I shared the recent developments, assuring him shewould be reunited with her studies once the school yearbegan.

"I can hardly contain myself," he confessed with a sigh, the weight of his longing evident in his words. "I ache for Fadia, and every moment apart feels like aneternity of torment."

"I yearn to see her," he pleaded earnestly. "Please, deliver this message to her."

How he looked at me, his head slightly inclined andthen turning away, was nothing short of heartrending. He resembled a bewildered and wounded lover; his pride and self-possession shattered as thoroughly as histragically broken heart.

Later that day, I handed her Tarek's heartfelt message.As her fingertips brushed the note, it was as if her soul took flight, lifted by her soaring heart. Her eyesshimmered with emotion as she absorbed the words,each soaked in Tarek's teardrops.

Then she turned to me, her gaze imploring. "You must assist me," she implored. "I yearn to see him, please help.

"With trembling hands and a heart brimming with emotion, she unfolded the parchment of his love for her."

DEAR FADIA

*In a realm where love's embrace is boundless, My heart,
like a child's, knows only tenderness, A majestic devotion
akin to faith's eternal dance,In your name, I find both
boundary and refuge.*

*In the depths of your eyes, a universe unfolds, Lost
within the infinite expanse of your spirit,Each day
without you stretches into eternity, A symphony of
longing echoing in my soul.*

*Your smile, a sunbeam piercing through shadows,Your
laughter, a melody that resonates within,
Kindness, the balm for my tormented heart, Your presence alone,a healer
of wounded spirits.*

*Let us rendezvous at Sam's Ice Cream Shop, This
Sunday, at the stroke of two, let us meet,Amidst the
sweetness of frozen delights,
Our love shall illuminate the world anew.*

As she read Tarek's heartfelt poem, it became undeniably clear what I had only suspected before Fate, often uncontrollable and bitter, sometimes even cruel, held sway over our lives. My heart ached for Fadia. But in the face of such a relentless force, what choice did we have but to accept our destinies?

Their story bore an uncanny resemblance to that of Romeo and Juliet, two star-crossed lovers whose tragic end seemed preordained. Yet, as a friend, what words could I offer? What actions could I take to mend my friend's heartache and heartbreak? I concluded that I must stand by her side and accompany her on this fateful rendezvous with Tarek.

When Sunday finally arrived, it brought an electric anticipation that seemed to charge the air around us. I approached Fadia's parents, requesting permission for a leisurely walk with my dear friend, suggesting we might savor the simple pleasure of ice cream on this sunny day. They granted their consent, blissfully unaware of our covert mission.

As we entered Sam's ice cream shop, time seemed to slow, and the world around us faded into insignificance. The ambiance was cozy, with the sweet aroma of freshly churned ice cream filling the air. But what indeed dominated the scene were Tarek and Fadia, two souls eternally entwined in love as fiercely as forbidden.

Their eyes met, and in that moment, the world disappeared. The intensity of their longing was palpable, like a wildfire waiting to consume everything in its path. Words were unnecessary; their gazes spoke volumes, conveying a depth of emotion that words could never capture.

Their fingers brushed as they reached for the same menu, igniting a spark that sent shivers down their spines. It was a touch transcending the physical, a connection born of a love that had weathered stormsand defied conventions.

And as they savored their ice cream, each bite was an intimate exchange, a stolen kiss of sweetness that mirrored the tenderness of their hearts. It was amoment frozen in time, a testament to the power of love, as raw and untamed as the universe itself. In that charming ice cream shop, Tarek and Fadia shared a moment that seemed to transcend the very essence oftime. Tears of longing transformed into peals of laughter, and their hands, once kept apart by cruel circumstances, now found solace in the gentle grasp of one another. Their fingers intertwined as if making a solemn promise to never let go. Together, they relishedthe sweetness of their ice cream, turning it into a communion of hearts.

As the hours effortlessly slipped away, cocooned in the warmth of their connection, the world around them blurred into insignificance. It was a timeless interlude, a sacred pause in their tumultuous journey.But alas, even the most magical moments must yield to the ticking clock. With reluctant smiles, they parted ways, exchanging words that resonated with heartfelt sincerity.

The journey back home unfolded as a stark contrastto the one that had led us there. Fadia's joy and newfound hope emanated from her like a radiant glow.She glided along the path, her feet seemingly hovering above the ground, and her eyes sparkled with the anticipation of their next encounter. It was as if her happiness had permeated everything around us—the trees, the bushes, even the covert—all seemed to baskin the warmth of her euphoria, except her mother.

Her mother, keenly observant, noticed the sudden metamorphosis in her daughter. The once quiet and sorrowful Fadia had blossomed into a vibrant and joyous version of herself. The eyes, often referred to aswindows to the soul, betrayed Fadia's uncontainablehappiness. Her mother sensed it, and deep down, sheunderstood. If only I could have shielded her from thestorm ahead, I pondered as we continued our journey,the weight of impending challenges lingering in the air.

On a rainy Sunday afternoon, Fadia stepped from the car that her parents had driven her in at approximately one o'clock. However, when I observed that there was a tense environment, my initial aspirations of having a pleasant Sunday lunch were completely destroyed. Herred-rimmed eyes reflected the misery that was going oninside of her, and she appeared to be in a state of agonizing sadness.

The moment our eyes met, she broke the silence byopening the car window and waved through tears. It was a heartbreaking departure. I stood there, unable to move, witnessing a display of agony, absolutely bewildered and unable to fathom the tragedy that wasslowly unfolding before me. Fadia's absence became increasingly distressing as the days passed. I was overcome with the agony of doubt, and I found myself walking around the balcony, praying for her return orany information that may shed light on the situation.The suspense was affecting my spirit.

I confronted my mother because I was driven by desperation. "Fadia is finally safe," she said, which hit close to home. The claimed "insanity" of dating a Muslim man has resulted in her being sent away to aconvent in order to heal from the situation. I am relieved to say that it was not you. Soon, she will neverremember him.

The indifference with which those remarks were made struck me like a gust of wind. A primordial crycame from me, a roar of disbelief and dismay reverberating through the atmosphere. How can theyconfine love, which is the cosmic karmic tie betweensouls, to such a narrow scope? For two hearts to be regarded acceptable, each of them must share the samebelief. What god did they pray to, and where was the supposed mercy in severing the bonds of two souls thatwere obviously destined to be together even though they were separated? Each reverberation served as aharsh reminder of an unjust separation, and it was accompanied by the reverberation of unattended queries.

CHAPTER XVII

JOURNEYS OF DISCOVERY: UNRAVELING THE TAPESTRY OF FAITH

In reflecting on religion, I find myself drawn to a fundamental question: what truly sets us apart? Are we not all interconnected, stemming from the same source and sharing a common humanity? It strikes me as absurd that we allow ourselves to be defined and divided by arbitrary labels—whether Muslim, Christian, Druze, or any other.

My journey of understanding has taken me from the narrow confines of childhood indoctrination to a broader perspective rooted in critical thinking and empathy. Growing up, I was fed harmful stereotypes and prejudices that later proved baseless and unkind. Why do we allow ourselves to be indoctrinated with hatred when the teachings of prophets universally preach love and compassion?

The fractures among religions and the conflicts they engender are often born from human failings—ego, fear, and the quest for power. But beneath these divisions lies a common thread of peace, empathy, and respect for all life.

I yearn for a world where we celebrate our differencesrather than allowing them to separate us. We must strive for unity and understanding, recognizing that despite our diverse beliefs, we are all connected by a shared humanity and a universal source of love.

Ultimately, not the label we wear defines us, but thevalues we embody. I firmly believe that God is one andthat divine presence is accessible to all, regardless of religious affiliation. We must embrace this truth andwork together towards a future of unity, compassion,and mutual respect.

CHAPTER XVIII

BEYOND BELIEF: A JOURNEY THROUGH TIME, FAITH, AND HUMANEMOTION

"This anger that I felt drew me to uncharted territories, where beneath the surface turbulence, lay theseeds of profound understanding."

"As I channeled my anger wisely, it became a torchlight guiding me through the labyrinth of my emotions, illuminating hidden truths and leading me to unexpected discoveries. Deeply disillusioned after Fadia's event, I embarked on a quest for truth, lettingthe flames of my fury drive me forward. This journeyled me down winding paths of history, delving deep into the annals of religion and politics."

In my pursuit, I uncovered tales as ancient as time itself. From the obscure realms of Zurvanism to the vibrant tapestry of Hinduism and Buddhism, the panorama of faith unfolded before me. Yet, it was the enigmatic figure of Thoth, the legendary Egyptian sage,who beckoned me further into the labyrinth of the past.

Then I broke away from all Narrowing beliefs and constitutions.

Thoth, renowned since antiquity for his infinite wisdom, becamethe focus of my investigation. His name has echoed across history, veiled in myth and legend, from the dawn of civilization. It was thought that he bequeathed wisdom to humans, from astronomical riddles to religious rites.

But the story didn't stop there. In a distant age, a conqueroremerged, wearing the mantle of Alexander the Great. Inspiredby Aristotle's ideas, he set out on a grand quest to unite regions and peoples under the flag of tolerance and wisdom.

Alexandria, a beacon of diversity and wisdom, lay at the heart of this expanding empire. Scholars from all over the world gathered in its hallowed halls to share thoughts and views in a spirit of brotherhood. The famed Library of Alexandria emerged here, symbolizing humanity's hunger for knowledge.

However, as history frequently shows, the shadows of avarice and ambition loomed large. With the rise of the Christian Holy Roman Empire, the tide started to turn. The once-celebrated achievements of antiquity were destroyed by fanaticism, withpagan temples desecrated and library treasures set ablaze.

The aftermath of this turmoil laid the groundwork for an epic drama. Across continents and ages, religions clashed, with each party claiming the holy mantle of truth. Despite the clamor of clashing voices, one question remained unanswered.

Why, in the name of gods who preached love and mercy, did mankind persist in sowing the fundamental interconnectedness that binds us together as one human family.

My encounters with Fadia may have been fleeting, but my ongoing interactions with Tarek remind me of the importance of engaging with diverse perspectives. Through these encounters, I continue to explore the profound truth that unity is not found in uniformity but rather in the rich tapestry of diversity that defines the human experience.

In a world where so many seek simplistic answers to life's complex questions, let us not forget the boundless beauty and wisdom inherent in embracing the full spectrum of existence. After all, the universe is our common heritage, and we can truly thrive as a species by recognizing and celebrating our interconnectedness.

Tarek and I had a singular mission: uncover the truth behind Fadia's mysterious disappearance and subsequent seclusion. After tireless efforts, we finally unearthed the name of the convent where Fadia had been taken - the Saydet Qannoubine Convent, located roughly an hour's drive away. With resolve in our hearts, we set out to visit her, though my motivations were driven by a desire to see her once more.

As we embarked on the journey, the atmosphere in the car was thick with tension.

Neither Tarek nor I exchanged a word; thoughts of Fadia consumed our minds. The grip of Tarek's hands on the steering wheel betrayed the turmoil within him, his knuckles white with the strain. The passing scenery seemed to blur into insignificance, mere background noise to our shared preoccupation.

With each passing mile, my heart pounded louder in my chest. The anticipation of seeing Fadia again after so long filled me with a mix of anxiety and longing.

Would she be safe? Would she still be the same spirited woman I remembered, or had the walls of her confinement taken their toll?

Eventually, we arrived at our destination, the convent looming before us like a silent sentinel atop a hill. It exuded an air of solemn beauty built into the rugged rock face and adorned with centuries-old frescoes. Yet, beneath its serene facade, I sensed the weight of Fadia's captivity.

Parking the car along a narrow street, we gazed up at the imposing structure. Though outwardly magnificent, I couldn't help but feel a pang of sorrow for Fadia. To her, this place represented not sanctuary but imprisonment - a gilded cage that held her dreams in chains. As we prepared to enter, my heart ached with the hope that we could somehow bring light to her darkness and set her free from the bonds that held her captive.

The hike to the front entry of Deir Qannoubine was an arduous journey, the rocky terrain stretching before us as we pressed on. As we trudged along the winding path, I couldn't shake the feeling of anticipation mixed with trepidation. The history of this place weighed heavily on my mind, knowing it once served as a fortress-palace for the Maronite Patriarchs, its walls steeped in centuries of tradition and secrecy.

Finally, after a grueling fifteen-minute hike, we reached the entrance, a massive stone archway that seemed to stretch toward the heavens. It is said that within these hallowed halls lay the preserved body of one of the patriarchs, a testament to the enduring legacy of this sacred site.

As we stepped inside, the cool air of the cavernous space enveloped us, carrying the scent of wildflowers and earth. For a moment, I closed my eyes and allowed myself to be transported by the memory of this place, a sanctuary amidst the world's chaos.

But our reverie was interrupted by the arrival of a sister, her grey habit a stark contrast against the rugged backdrop. With a lumbering gait, she approached us, her presence commanding yet gentle.

"Can I help you?" she inquired, her voice soft but authoritative.

My heart raced as I uttered the words that had brought us here. "Yes, I am looking to visit my friend Fadia."

For a moment, there was silence as the sister considered my request. Then, with a nod, she turned and disappeared into the depths of the convent, leaving us to wait in tense anticipation. Minutes passed like hours as we stood beneath the towering archway, the weight of uncertainty pressing down upon us. And then, like a sudden thunderclap, her words shattered the silence.

"Visits are forbidden," she said simply, her tone final and resolute.

It was as though a heavy weight had descended upon me, crushing my hopes and leaving me adrift in a seaof despair. With a heavy heart, I watched as the sisterturned and retreated into the shadows, leaving us aloneonce more.

As we stood there in the quietude of the cavern, I couldn't help but feel a sense of profound loss. The sanctuary I had longed to revisit had become a symbol of my friend's captivity, a barrier between us that seemed impossible. And yet, even in the face of suchadversity, I knew that I would not rest until I had found a way to break through the walls that held her prisoner.

Disappointment hung heavy between us as we returned, our footsteps echoing against the rockyterrain. Thanking the nun for her efforts, we turned away from the convent, our hearts heavy with uncertainty. The drive home was sad, the weight of our unanswered questions pressing down upon us like a suffocating blanket.

With clouded thoughts and heavy hearts, we climbed back into the car. Tarek's frustration boiled over, his hands covering his face as he uttered a primal screamof anguish. The sound reverberated through the car, jolting me from my thoughts as he pounded thesteering wheel in frustration. For a terrifying moment,I feared the car would careen off the winding mountainroad and plunge into the valley below.

But as quickly as his anger had erupted, it subsided,leaving only tears in its wake. In the silence that followed, each of us was left alone with our pain, theweight of our emotions filling the cramped confines of the car. As we drove back home, the road stretching out endlessly before us, I couldn't help but wonder what tomorrow would bring - and how long it mightbe before we saw Fadia again.

The pitter-patter of raindrops against my window stirred memories within me, memories of a story etched in tears and pain. Fadia's tale, with its echoes of love and suffering, lingered in my mind like the scentof rain on parched earth. How remarkable, I thought,that a single sense could evoke such a myriad of emotions and recollections.

Tarek and I remained in contact for nearly two months, bound by our shared hope for Fadia's return.Each day, he would venture back to the convent, hisheart heavy with longing, his spirit buoyed by the faintest glimmer of possibility. But as the days stretched into weeks and the weeks into months, the walls of that ancient sanctuary grew ever more impenetrable, suffocating his hopes and dreams.

In his eyes, I saw the anguish of a man torn betweenlove and despair, his soul hardened by the relentless grip of religious dogma. Once a symbol of faith and devotion, the convent had become a prison of his own making, its ancient stones weighing heavy on his spirit.

And then, in a moment of heart-wrenching clarity, Tarek made his decision. He came to me one last time, his eyes burning with a fire born of anger and vengeance. With a heavy heart, he bid me farewell, hispath now set on a darker journey.

I watched him go, a sense of foreboding settling over me like a shroud. In the aftermath of his departure, I found myself adrift, the echoes of his words haunting me like a ghostly refrain. And as the war engulfed Lebanon in its deadly embrace, I knew that I, too, had to seek solace elsewhere, leaving behind the shattered remnants of a life once lived.

Book II

CHAPTER XIX

SEEDS OF UNDERSTANDING

"Memories are the threads of time we weave into the quilt of our existence, stitching together the past, present, and future with the essence of who we are."

Memories swirl around me like leaves caught in a storm, each one a whisper of what once was and what could have been. Thoughts, too, dance in the tumult of my mind, blending with questions of possibility and fate. What if I wonder if the past is not just a distant memory but the cause of our present reality? And if so, what does that make of today?

Today is the canvas upon which we paint the picture of our future. It is a blank slate, waiting to be shaped by our actions and decisions. The past may have set us on a particular course, but it is in the present moment that we hold the power to change our trajectory.

Yet, amidst these musings, a nagging question persists: what if we are but victims of circumstance, tossed about by the whims of fate? What if the storms of life batter our boat, throwing us off course and onto an unfamiliar shore?

Fear grips our hearts amid chaos, and the urge to abandon ship grows stronger. But what if we hold on,weathering the storm until it passes? What if, in the calm that follows, we find ourselves in uncharted waters, faced with the daunting task of starting anew?

It is a daunting prospect, to be sure. But it is also a chance for growth and renewal. In the face of adversity,we discover our true strength and resilience. And so, Icling to the hope that even in the darkest of storms, there lies the promise of a brighter tomorrow, waitingto be seized with both hands.

We were once four inseparable friends, bound together by laughter and shared dreams. But when the storm of war broke upon us, we found ourselves tornapart, scattered like leaves in the wind. Monstrous waves of hatred and anger crashed against the fragile vessel of our friendship, leaving only shattered fragments in their wake. Conflict and bloodshed dissolved our dreams, leaving behind only the stark reality of survival.

As I grappled with the remnants of our fractured bond in the aftermath, I often found myself entwined with my solitude. It became a constant companion, faithful as a shadow, trailing me through the rooms ofmy home. I gleaned profound lessons in its silent company, shedding tears that harkened back to bygone days when innocence was our guiding light. Mysolitude and I forged a new path guided by the echoesof our shared past and the promise of a brighter tomorrow. As I faced the unknown horizon with trepidation and hope, I carried the lessons learned in the crucible of loneliness, a testament to the enduringpower of the human spirit.

Then, like a bolt of lightning illuminating the darkness, an idea struck me: why not seek them out?Could they be just around the corner, waiting to be found? The notion sent a surge of anticipation coursingthrough me, mingled with a nervous energy thatseemed to warp time itself, hastening and slowing like a cat on the prowl, attuned to the faintest rustle in thewalls.

Thankful for the technological marvels of our time, I delved into social media with fervent determination. Countless names with the same family surname flooded my screen, leaving me to wonder: what if they had taken on their spouse's name? How would I everlocate them amidst this sea of possibilities?

Undeterred, I scrutinized each face, mindful that timehas a way of sculpting features, perhaps even throughthe artifice of cosmetic enhancements. Hours passed unnoticed as I persisted in my search, time holding itsbreath in deference to my quest.

And then, there she was—Anna. Though adorned with subtle updates, her smile and eyes remained unmistakably hers. Her hair is unchanged. A photograph captured her amidst a group of unfamiliarfaces—friends or family, it was hard to discern. Yet,undeterred, I scoured their expressions, seeking a flicker of recognition. Alas, none came.

THEN,

A tremor of excitement rippled down my spine, adrenaline coursing through my veins as I clicked onher image and then navigated to her profile page. With a determined click, I sent a friend request, a small gesture in pursuit of reconnection.

My eyes drank in the familiar images of her smiling face. There she was, as beautiful as ever, her photos documenting her adventures worldwide. It was abittersweet moment, filled with nostalgia for the past.Though muted, the hope for the future. Perhaps,through finally reconnecting with the others to bridgethe gap that had kept us apart for so long.

As I sat by the window, savoring the rich taste of thewine and stillness contemplation, I couldn't shake the feeling of being caught in a whirlwind of emotions. The scenes of the past played out before my eyes like a movie, each frame a vivid snapshot of moments long gone. Laughter and cries intertwined in a haunting melody, stirring memories that lay dormant in the recesses of my mind.

What drove me to revisit the past, to sift through thesands of time in search of answers that may never come? Was it a longing for closure, a desire to makesense of the fragments of my past? Or it was simply theallure of Ofgrita, drawing me back to a time when life seemed more straightforward, and the future held endless possibilities.

As I pondered these questions, I realized that life wasa never-ending journey of discovery, a labyrinth of twists and turns with no clear path forward. And yet,despite the uncertainty that lay ahead, there was a certain comfort in knowing that each new day brought with it the promise of new beginnings.

With the last drops of wine lingering on my lips, I made my way to bed, the soft embrace of my pillow a welcome refuge from the tumult of my thoughts. As sleep claimed me, I drifted into dreams filled with whispers of the past and hopes for the future, ready to face whatever tomorrow may bring.

CHAPTER XX

STITCHES OF IDENTITY

"Echoes of Resilience: Lessons from Friendship and Solitude"

What is the past other than faded memories? Once, they were vivid and colorful; now, they are Smokey black-and-white remembrances tinged with time. Though muted, the feelings they evoke are still present, residing within the chambers of our hearts. Tender, sometimes sad and unpleasant, they serve as reminders of joyful and sorrowful experiences.

In the quietness of solitude, amidst the vast ocean of introspection, one finds solace in the depths of their being. Aging, far from a decline, is an awakening - graduation from the school of Life, though the pursuit of wisdom continues, akin to seeking a master's degree.

From the stories of my friends, I gleaned invaluable lessons, particularly about the resilience of women in the face of suffering, abuse, and prejudice. Each of them bore witness to the trials of life, navigating the treacherous waters of love and deception with varying degrees of grace and grit. Their experiences served as a testament to the indomitable strength of the human spirit, inspiring me to navigate my journey with courage and resilience.

Each passing minute felt like an eternity as I anxiously checked my phone, my heart pounding with anticipation. I couldn't bear the thought of missing even a notification, so I cranked up the volume, hoping for any sign from Anna. But as one day turned into two and then three, doubt gnawed at my insides. Was Anna deliberately avoiding me? Had she moved on, leaving our shared past behind? The mere idea sent waves of sorrow and self-reproach crashing over me. Despite the growing uncertainty, I clung to my phone as if it were my only tether to hope in a sea of doubt.

Finally, on the fourth day, the notification I'd anxiously awaited flashed across my screen., Adorned with hearts and kisses, Anna's response filled me with excitement and relief. Quickly, I messaged her on Messenger, asking if she was available for a call.

Her enthusiastic reply, "Yes, absolutely," accompanied by a heart symbol, spurred me into action. I dialed her number, my heart racing with anticipation. As she picked up, my breath hitched in my chest, but I managed to steady myself enough to speak. We dove into conversation, each eager to catch up on lost time, our words tumbling over each other in haste.

Then, gathering my courage, I shared my heartfelt thoughts with Anna. "During this pandemic lockdown," I confessed, "I've found myself yearning for the days of our youth, missing our friendship deeply. True friendship, to me, means growing individually yet staying close. So, I thought, why not reconnect with everyone through Zoom? We could update each other on our lives and share stories... Whatdo you think?" The response was music to my ears. "Oh, I would love to," Anna exclaimed.

"Could you help me find the others?" I asked eagerly."You got it," she replied, her enthusiasm contagious. With plans in motion, excitement bubbled within me.
"Okay then, I'll eagerly await your call," I said excitedly.
"I can't wait."

I found myself drawn back to my favorite spot in thekitchen, nestled by the window overlooking the oncelush vineyard., I gazed out at it, now a desolate tableauof grey. The once vibrant vines, now skeletal and fragile, whispered tales of a past life, clinging desperately to hope beneath winter's cold embrace. As the wind danced through the barren rows, it carried a bittersweet symphony of memories, whisking me back to the day I first set foot in the South of France, handin hand with Alain Dupres.

Each memory sprang into existence like a star in thesky, competing with the others to be the center of focus as we reminisced about happier times. Every thread in the tapestry of my life interweaves moments of joy, sadness, and everything in between, and I wondered which memory I would choose to recall onmy final day.

But amidst the patchwork of my past, one figure stood out in bold relief: Alain. It was at my father's workplace amidst the rolling hills of the Kurma Vineyard in the Bekaa Valley where our love story unfolded. My father's role as the vineyard's sales manager and quality control inspector brought us together, igniting a passion that would shape the courseof my existence.

Memories, I realized, are the lifeblood of our being,each one a testament to the richness of human experience. For me, the memory that resonated mostdeeply was that of my first love, imbued with the sun'swarmth, the scent of ripe grapes, and the tenderembrace of Alain.

My father's workplace, nestled amidst the breathtaking beauty of the Kurma Vineyard in the Bekaa Valley, served as the canvas for a spontaneous burst of vibrancy that would forever etch itself into mymemory. He labored tirelessly as the vineyard's sales manager and quality control inspector, a role that unknowingly set the stage for a serendipitousencounter that would change everything.

On that particular day, an impulsive urge seized me,urging me to surprise my father with an unexpected visit. Eager to inject a splash of excitement into the day,I decided that a glass of wine would be the perfect catalyst. Draped in my favorite summer yellow jumpsuit, I took a moment to brush my hair until it gleamed, tying it up in a carefree ponytail that danced in the breeze. The vibrant hue of my attire perfectly mirrored the radiant energy of the summer season, infusing me with a sense of buoyancy and joy.

Setting out on the journey to the vineyard, I rolled down the windows of my car, aching, welcoming thecrisp mountain air that enveloped me. There's an enchanting quality to the wind in the mountains—it rushes towards you with bold confidence, its touch assoft as a lover's caress. It weaves through the verdant foliage, whispering secrets to the trees and carrying theheady scent of ripening grapes.

As I drove, I immersed myself in the landscape's kaleidoscope of colors. The trees swayed gracefully in the wind, their leaves ablaze with crimson, gold, andemerald green hues. The melodic chirping of birds provided the perfect accompaniment to my journey, their joyful songs filling the air with a symphony of sound.

At that moment, surrounded by the majesty of nature's palette and the soothing embrace of the wind,I felt a profound sense of peace wash over me. It wasas though I had been transported to a world of pure serenity, where time stood still and every moment was a celebration of life's vibrant tapestry.

I parked the car, the crunch of gravel beneath my feetechoing through the quiet vineyard. Stepping out, I made my way through the rows of trees and parked cars, the anticipation building with each step.

As I approached my father's office, I saw himstanding amidst the wine barrels, their sturdy forms lined up like soldiers awaiting their commander's orders.

The air was thick with the intoxicating aroma of wine,swirling around me like a mesmerizing fog. I felt intoxicated by its heady scent, my senses swimming in a haze of anticipation. "Surprise!" I exclaimed, unable to contain my excitement.

My father turned, his face breaking into a wide grin atthe sight of me. "Wow, what a pleasant surprise," hereplied warmly, his eyes twinkling with delight.

"I came to see you and spend some time together. Maybe we can share a glass of wine?" I suggested eagerly.

"Sure, but only one, promise?" he teased, a twinkle of mischief in his eyes.

"I promise," I said with a smile, my heart swelling with affection.

He disappeared into his office briefly, returning moments later with two crystal glasses reserved for special occasions. As he poured the wine, I couldn'thelp but admire him—the very essence of a grapevine himself. Medium in height with rounded shoulders, he exuded a quiet strength reminiscent of the sturdy trunk of a grapevine. His hands, weathered and calloused from years of hard work, were a testament to his dedication to his craft.

But his eyes captured my attention the most—wideand dark green, like the mighty rivers of the Amazon,with a warmth that radiated from their depths. His hair, once dark, was now streaked with grey, a badge of honor earned through years of experience. And though he may have carried a bit of extra weight around his waist, it only added to his charm, a testament to a lifewell-lived and savored.

As we raised our glasses in a toast, I couldn't help butfeel grateful for this moment—for the chance to sharea glass of wine with my father and to bask in the warmth of his love and affection.

Looking at my father, standing there amidst the familiar surroundings of the vineyard, I couldn't helpbut feel a sense of peace wash over me. His presencewas like a warm embrace, wrapping me in a cocoon of safety and contentment.

"Please, let me tap the chalices before you pour thewine," I requested, a smile playing at the corners of mylips. "You know how much I love the sound of crystal and the melody it emits. It sings my favorite songs."

"Walk with me," he said, his voice gentle yet filled with purpose.

Following him a few steps, we came to rest by an oldbarrel, weathered with age yet still standing strong. As he looked at me with pride and satisfaction, he deftlyheld the glass beneath the barrel tap and began to pour.

The wine flowed into the glasses like a sacredoffering, the rich aroma filling the air with its intoxicating fragrance. With practiced ease, we began the ritual of swirling, sniffing, and tasting, each step atestament to our reverence for this ancient elixir. "Hmm, excellent," he murmured, his eyes twinkling with delight. "Here, smell it and try to decipher the aroma."

"Formidable," I replied, taking a moment to savor thescent wafting from the glass. "I would say it's a mix ofspices and herbs, with a strong scent of bay leaves and rosemary, correct?"

"Exactly," he exclaimed, his voice filled with pride. "You could be a sommelier now. Fille de papa."

And so began my private lessons in the art of wine appreciation. His passion for the subject was palpableas he spoke, his words infused with years of experienceand wisdom.

"Wine, wine, wine!" he exclaimed, his voice rising enthusiastically. "It is alive, the elixir of youth. Remember, it is made with years of labor, care, and centuries of experience when you drink it."

As he spoke, memories of days gone by flooded mymind— the joyous moments spent picking grapes with my parents and friends, the laughter and camaraderiethat filled the air during harvest season.

Those memories etched into every fiber of my being reminded me of the rich tapestry of life and the enduring bond between family, tradition, and the land.

As I listened to my father's words, I couldn't help butfeel grateful for the legacy he had passed down to meand the countless lessons I had yet to learn.

This day will forever be ingrained in my memory, marked by a heartwarming surprise that unfolded unexpectedly. It all began with my intention to surprisemy father, a man who has always been a pillar of support in my life. Little did I know that the tables would turn, and my father would be surprised by hisown friends.

As I entered my father's office, I was filled with anticipation, eager to see the joy on his face as he discovered my presence. However, to my delight, I soon realized I wasn't the only one with plans to surprise him. A couple around his age entered the room, and a young man greeted my father in fluent French.

Their unexpected arrival added an extra layer of excitement to the day, turning what was meant to be asimple surprise into a memorable gathering of friends. Amidst the flurry of greetings and introductions, my father's friends shared stories and caught up on old times, their laughter filling the room with warmth and camaraderie.

And then, as if the day couldn't get any better, my father turned to me with a smile of realization. "Let meintroduce my daughter," he exclaimed, his voice brimming with pride. "This is Camille," he said,gesturing towards me, "and this is my friend Pierre andhis wife, Jeanette."

As I exchanged greetings with Pierre and Jeanette, Icouldn't help but feel overwhelmed by the sense of belonging and camaraderie in the room. And when Pierre proudly introduced his son, Alain, the circle felt complete, a testament to the enduring bonds of friendship and family.

As the afternoon progressed, it became clear that this impromptu reunion was special. The bond between myfather and his friends and the introduction of Alain andmyself added warmth and meaning to the day. As weeventually made plans to continue our celebration overlunch at a nearby restaurant, I couldn't help but feel grateful for the opportunity to be surrounded by suchlove and companionship.

CHAPTER XXI

ALAIN

Amid a picturesque outdoor setting, I found myself captivated by a man who could easily pass as Brad Pitt'stwin. His golden locks, reminiscent of Achilles himself,were impeccably styled, framing his flawlessly proportioned features. His eyes sparkled with claritylike a mountain stream, drawing me in with their magnetic allure. It was impossible to tear my gaze away from him, and I couldn't help but feel a flush of embarrassment as I suspected he had noticed my admiration.

Seated at an outdoor restaurant, we were envelopedby a gentle breeze that caressed our bodies with its soothing touch.

Overhead, the branches of nearby trees formed a protective canopy, shielding us from the sun's harshglare and creating an intimate ambiance.

A veritable banquet of exquisite foods lay before us,befitting a king or queen. From savory treats like Koftaand Chenklish to traditional Lebanese mezze like BabaGhanouj and Tabbouleh, the table was covered with a variety of flavors and textures. The gastronomic spectacle was elevated with grilled seafood, meats, and unusual dishes such as escargot and Grenouille.

As rounds of Arak, a potent alcoholic beverage, were served, I felt my inhibitions begin to melt away. With each sip, my shyness evaporated, replaced by a newfound sense of confidence and humor. I found myself engaging in lively conversation, effortlessly drawn into Alain's magnetic presence. In that moment, surrounded by good food, good company, and the intoxicating allure of Arak, I surrendered to the enchantment of the evening, allowing myself to be swept away by Alain's charm and beauty.

For me, it was love at first sight. His eyes, illuminated by the effects of the alcohol, sparkled like diamonds in the dimly lit ambiance. I sensed a mesmerizing blend of sensuality and radiance in their depths, drawing me in with an irresistible allure.

He possesses the sturdy build of a knight, his frame exuding an aura of strength and protection that makes me feel safe and secure in his presence.

As the alcohol began to take effect, we found ourselves shedding the layers of pretense and inhibition, allowing our true selves to emerge. It was as if we had cast aside our masks, stripped off our metaphorical clothes, and stood before each other in a state of raw vulnerability, akin to Adam and Eve in the Garden of Eden.

Despite our initial encounter as strangers, the night unfolded with familiarity and camaraderie, as if we had known each other for years. It was a curious transformation, leaving us more connected than ever.

Before parting ways, we made plans to embark on a tour of the Bekaa Valley the following day, eager to explore the small towns and hidden gems that dotted the picturesque landscape. As we bid each other farewell, there was a sense of excitement and anticipation for the adventures that lay ahead.

CHAPTER XXII

WHISPERS OF LOVE: A PARISIAN ROMANCE

Our love flourished, and we unearthed a treasure trove of shared passions and interests with each passing day. Together, we delved into the depths of ourinner child, reveling in playful antics, carefree laughter, and moments of pure joy that we stored in the albumof our minds.

Alain frequently visited Lebanon, just as I sporadically journeyed to Paris. On one such occasion, during oneof my trips, Alain surprised me with a delightful picnicbasket filled with all our favorite treats and a bottle ofBeaujolais Wine. We went to Square du Vert-Galantpark, nestled at the tip of Île de la Cité in the heart ofParis.

It was a scorching summer day on July 16th, 1985, theair thick with humidity as we sought refuge beneath theshade of the trees. Alain meticulously arranged our picnic spot, spreading out a soft cloth on the grass, fluffing up two pillows, and placing the picnic basketwith a gallant flourish.

On that day, my heart soared like a helium balloon, weightless and buoyant in the breeze. I can still recall the intoxicating scent of the air, laden with an aphrodisiac allure that seemed to envelop us. Every time Alain drew near, his fragrance teased my senses, sending shivers down my spine and enveloping me in a delightful chill.

His piercing blue eyes captivated me, each gaze deeper than the last, drawing me into a trance of affection and admiration. I realized the depth of my love for Paris, Alain, and the world in those moments.

Alain whisked me away to every corner of Paris, introducing me to its iconic landmarks and hidden gems. From strolls along the Avenue des Champs Élysées to awe-inspiring visits to the Musée du Louvre and the majestic Cathédrale Notre-Dame de Paris, our adventures were nothing short of magical.

But it wasn't just the cityscape that captivated us; we also explored the vineyards and countryside, indulging in exquisite Wine and savoring life's simple pleasures. These memories are etched into the fabric of our beings, woven into the very essence of our existence, as a constant reminder of our love and joy.

Ultimately, all we can do is embrace these memories, cherishing them as cherished companions on our journey through life.

The shrill ring of my phone pierced through the silence, and my heart leaped into my throat. With trembling hands, I answered, greeted by Anna's voice bubbling with excitement. She had found them, she exclaimed and arranged for a Zoom meeting next

Saturday at 6:30 PM. Despite the suddenness of the news, I couldn't contain my joy, eagerly agreeing to thereunion.

As I hung up the call, a surge of anticipation mixedwith anxiety flooded my senses. Five long days stretched ahead of me, each moment filled with restlessanticipation. Thoughts raced through my mind, conjuring up images of our long-lost friends and sharedmemories.

With a knot forming in my stomach and a sense of unease settling over me, I sought refuge in a glass ofwine. The rich aroma and comforting warmth of the drink offered a brief respite from my turbulent emotions, but the underlying anxiety lingered, casting ashadow over my anticipation.

I returned to my kitchen and brewed a fresh cup ofcoffee, the rich aroma enveloping me like a warm embrace. With each swirl of steam rising from the mug,I felt a sense of comfort and familiarity, like reconnecting with an old friend. Grasping the cup, I went to the window, where memories and reflectionsoften converged.

They say that the eyes are the window to the soul, butthe view from my window speaks volumes for me. It's a portal to my past, present, and future, where each passing moment leaves an indelible mark on my heart. Today, it prompted me to revisit a long-forgotten letterthat in a peaceful gathering, the four of us decided towrite a letter to our future selves and check for our accomplishments or if our dreams came true. We were fifteen years old.

I retrieved the letter from its hiding place in an old trunk with nostalgia and curiosity. It was a testament to youthful dreams and aspirations, a reminder of the journey I had embarked upon many years ago. As I unfolded the faded paper, the aroma of coffee mingled with the scent of memories, creating a tapestry of emotions that warmed me.

Dear Me, June 1978,

As you open this letter, take a moment to reflect on what you have achieved thus far in your journey through life. Remind yourself of the dreams and aspirations you've held dear, and consider how far you've come in turning those dreams into reality.

1. *Love: Have you found the kind of love you've always dreamed of?*
2. *Writing: Your passion for writing has been a driving force in your life.*
3. *Travel and Learning: Did you travel??*
4. *Friendship: Your friendships have been a source of joy, support, and laughter. How did it go?*

Luxury and Living: Consider the life you're living now and how it aligns with the vision of luxury and beauty you've envisioned.

I was transported back in time as a torrent of memories swept over my head as I turned my face. As I thought back on those times of complete joy when it appeared like we would live happily ever after, tears started to form in my eyes.

Before the meeting, I settled in front of my makeuptable, taking a moment to assess myself in the mirror.How do I look now? How much have I changed sincewe last met? Has time left its mark on me? Concerns flooded my mind as I scrutinized my appearance, mainly focusing on my eyes, the windows to my soul.They needed framing, I decided. With my black eyepencil, I traced a bold contour around them, adding atouch of blush and lipstick to complete the look.

After adjusting my hair into a tight ponytail, I paused,wary of pulling too hard and accentuating any signs of aging. Silly as it may seem, I spritzed my preferred perfume, hoping it would make its presence feltthrough the screen. At 6:15 PM, I eagerly logged intoZoom, entering the meeting password. As I joined the call, I couldn't help but feel a rush of excitement.

Three familiar faces from the past greeted me, reminiscent of characters from the beloved Star Trekseries I adored. It was as if we were crew members communicating through screens, transported to another world. Euphoria, screams, laughter, and tearsfilled the virtual room, creating a chaotic yet nostalgic atmosphere. Conversations overlapped, echoing memories of our teenage years. Despite the confusion, reconnecting with old friends was joyful, reminiscent of the camaraderie shared on the Starship Enterprise.

I gazed at the three faces before me, feeling surprisedand curious. With Anna seated to my left, I tilted myhead slightly, studying her features for any traces of ourshared past. However, it was Fadia who truly captured my attention. Clad in a nun's habit, she retained an air of innocence, her long black hair possibly hidden beneath the chapel veil. Her eyebrows, shaped like swords, remained unchanged, contrasting her skin as smooth as velvet. "Fadia," I addressed her, my voice tinged with astonishment. "You became a nun."

As the evening unfolded, we delved into the depthsof our memories, recounting tales of our adventures,triumphs, and even our heartaches. With each story shared, the bond between us seemed to grow stronger, bridging the physical distance that had separated us forso long.

Anna reminisced about her travels worldwide, her photographs painting vivid images of far-off lands and exotic cultures. Fadia's tales of her life as a nun broughta sense of serenity and spirituality to the conversation, and I found myself captivated by the details of her journey.

Amidst the laughter and chatter, I felt a profound gratitude for these friendships that had endured the testof time. Despite the years that had passed and the pathswe had chosen, our connection remained as strong asever.

As the night wore on and the wine flowed freely, wemade plans for future reunions, promising not to let so much time pass between visits. As we bid each otherfarewell, I couldn't help but feel a sense of contentmentwash over me, knowing that no matter where life took us, we would always have these cherished memories tohold onto.

CHAPTER XXIII

FADIA

As Fadia shared her story, a heavy silence descended upon us, laden with her pain and sorrow. Each word she uttered seemed to carry a palpable sense of grief, filling the room with an atmosphere of somber reflection.

Our hearts ached in empathy as we listened intently, absorbing the depth of her suffering and the magnitude of her loss. No words could adequately express the depth of our sympathy, only a profound sense of solidarity and compassion that bound us together in shared sorrow.

In the wake of Tarek's tragic death on a suicidal mission, I found myself at a crossroads, grappling with profound grief and a sense of profound loss. It was a moment that demanded a decision that would shape the trajectory of my future in ways I couldn't yet comprehend.

At first, I sought solace in isolation, grappling with the weight of grief and loss. But as time passed, I discovered a new sense of purpose in helping orphaned and abandoned children who had been affected by the horrors of war.

Despite the pain lingering from my past, I've found a deep sense of inner peace in my mission. When asked about forgiveness, I've understood its profound importance in finding true peace and fulfillment in my work.

With a heavy heart and a mind clouded with turmoil,I made the difficult choice to sever ties with my familyand embark on a new path—one that led me to the solemn halls of the convent.

My journey is a testament to the resilience of the human spirit and the transformative power of forgiveness. Through these experiences, I've learned the true meaning of compassion and the profound impact it can have on others and myself.

ANNA

"Let me paint you a picture of my life, a tale woven with threads of resilience and newfound strength amidst the stormy seas of loss and betrayal.

Leaving the familiar shores of my hometown, I sought refuge in the bustling streets of Beirut, a city pulsating with life and possibility. With grit and determination, I carved a path for myself, finding solace in the halls of the French consulate, where my fluency in the language became my ticket to a better life.

But oh, how the tides turned when love knocked at my door. A whirlwind romance with a French diplomat swept me off my feet, and together, we soared to dizzying heights, exploring the far reaches of the globe hand in hand.

Yet, amidst the glittering lights of Hong Kong, darkness lurked in the shadows, ready to shatter the illusion of bliss. In a cruel twist of fate, I stumbled upon the painful truth of my partner's infidelity, tearing asunder the fragile faith of trust that bound us together.

With a heavy heart and shattered dreams, I made the agonizing decision to cut ties and return to the familiar embrace of my homeland. But in the ashes of betrayal, a phoenix rises, fueled by a newfound resolve to reclaim my destiny and forge a path toward For I vowed, with every fiber of my being, that I would not endure the same pain I had experienced with Nathan.

My heart may bear scars, but they are badges of honor, reminders of the battles I've fought and the victories yet to come. Moreover, while in Hong Kong,I made good money, which allowed me to purchase my own apartment and even venture into a successful real estate business. With each step, I'm reclaiming my independence and building a future on my own terms."

CHAPTER XXIV
MARIAM

"Child abuse, a cruel shadow cast upon innocence, inflicts wounds deeper than the flesh, leaving the soul trembling in the darkness of betrayal and anguish."

As I recount my journey, I can see the curiosity in your eyes, anxious to know the twists and turns that shaped my life.

I left My hometown with my mother and her boyfriend to USA in a tourist visa.

Opened a Middle Eastern Restaurant and we started a family business. Then it all began innocently enough, with him being a regular patron at the restaurant where I worked. Our interactions evolved from friendly banter over Mediterranean cuisine to a genuine connection. He exuded charm and warmth, drawing me in with his affable nature and witty humor.

As my visa expires in a couple of months, I was hopeful that marrying him would resolve my situation and allow me to get my green card.

Our friendship grew as we explored the vibrant streets of downtown Boston together. His presence brought me solace and joy, a welcome escape from thechallenges of my past.

With each passing day, our bond deepened, and I fell deeply in love. Our shared moments became cherished memories, filling my heart with happiness and belonging.

But then, reality shattered my blissful paradise. Theman I loved confessed that he was already married andhad deceived me with false promises of marriage. The revelation plunged me into a whirlwind of emotions,from anger to despair.

My once-idyllic world crumbled, leaving me to grapple with the pain of betrayal and broken trust. Despite the anguish, I held onto hope, believing that our love could conquer all obstacles.

For seven long years, I clung to the promise of a future together, enduring the agony of waiting for hisdivorce. Even in the face of mounting evidence of betrayal, I held onto the flicker of hope within me.

Finally, he obtained the promised divorce, and we exchanged vows of everlasting love. But doubt lingeredin my mind, a reminder of the pain I had endured. Wegot married, and two beautiful girls were the fruit ofour love.

Then, after a few years, cracks appeared in our seemingly perfect union. His escalating alcohol consumption transformed our home into a battleground of fights and abuse.

I couldn't bear to see my daughters grow up in sucha toxic environment, mirroring the chaos of my ownchildhood. So, with a heavy heart, I made the hardestdecision of my life—to leave.

As I walked away, memories of my father flooded back. I remembered the pain and turmoil of mychildhood, and I vowed to break the cycle of abuse for my own children.

And now, after years of resilience and hard work, Ihave built my own successful restaurant. It is a testament to my strength and determination to create a better life for myself and my daughters.

Ultimately, leaving was the most challenging and bestdecision I ever made. It taught me the importance ofself-love and resilience, and despite the pain, it pavedthe way for a brighter future for myself and my daughters.

CHAPTER XXV

MY TURN

"Loss with death: where grief becomes the silent companion of memories, and love becomes the bridge that connects the departed with the living, transcendingthe boundaries of mortality."

The day of our wedding remains etched as the highlight of my life. We exchanged vows in a quaintchurch nestled in Alain's picturesque village in the southwest of France, surrounded by their vineyards. It was a balmy day in May, filled with sunshine and gentlebreezes. Our ceremony was intimate, attended only by our parents, close friends, and me, floating on cloud nine.

Following the ceremony, we gathered in a charmingvineyard where Alain had arranged a delightful feast ofcharcuterie and an assortment of cheeses. It was a celebration filled with love and joy, a day I will foreverhold dear in my heart.

The house we shared became my sanctuary, where each day was a treasure. We were blessed with a daughter who pursued her passion in entomology, and I now have the joy of doting on my grandson, Jule.

But life took a heartbreaking turn when Alain began to withdraw into himself, slipping into a deep depression despite our efforts to help him. We sought the best psychiatric care, but nothing seemed to alleviate his pain. Then, one fateful day, I returned home to a devastating sight: Alain had taken his own life.

Since then, I've been grappling with grief while shouldering the responsibility of managing our vineyard alone. The loss of my beloved husband weighs heavy on my heart as I navigate this new reality.

In this journey of healing and rebuilding, I lean on the support of friends and family, seeking solace in shared memories and the beauty of the vineyard that was once our shared dream. Though the pain is profound, I strive to honor Alain's memory and find strength in our shared love, one day at a time.

The End

This is a biography of four friends, that shows Thestrength and power of women for rebirth, is like a phoenix rising, embodying resilience, determination, and the ability to turn adversity into opportunity. They inspire hope, drive change, and prove that from setbacks come triumphs.

As for Mariam what she had learned was:

Leaving wasn't easy, but I knew it was necessary for my well-being and the safety of my children. It was a journey into the unknown, filled with uncertainty and fear.

However, I found strength in putting myself first and prioritizing our happiness.

Anna said:

I stand tall on familiar soil, a beacon of resilience in the face of adversity. Forged in the crucible of heartache and loss, I emerge stronger, fiercer, ready to face whatever trials may lie ahead. And as I gaze upon the horizon, I do so with unwavering determination, knowing that the darkest nights give birth to the brightest stars.

Fadia's summery was:

My journey is a testament to the resilience of the women spirit and the transformative power of forgiveness. Through these experiences, I've learned the true meaning of compassion and the profound impact it can have on others and myself.

My Lesson:

The suicide of my spouse plunged me into a whirlwind of intense emotions, including shock, grief, guilt, anger, and confusion. I struggle to comprehendthe loss and grapple with overwhelming feelings of sadness and despair.

I have learned the importance of open and honest communication within relationships, including the ability to express concerns, seek help, and provide support.

I am a survivor, able to overcome adversity and navigate the depths of loss with courage and grace. Though the scars of my experience may persist, I refuseto be defined solely by tragedy. Instead, I worked on my recovery path as an opportunity for personalgrowth and progress.

ACKNOWLEDGMENT:

I want to offer my heartfelt gratitude to my dear friends. Your steadfast support and shared stories have meant more to me than I can say. We've set out on a journey of understanding, empathy, and empowerment because of our shared experiences.

It's been eye-opening to witness how, collectively, we've proven that when a woman decides to transformher life, she does so with unrivaled grit and determination. Your stories have illuminated the road, demonstrating that difficult times are not hurdles butrather vital learning experiences in our journey of progress.

Thank you for being pillars of support in my life. Thank you for sharing your vulnerabilities, successes, and all in between. I am immensely grateful for the strength and sisterhood we have made together.

Here's to continuing on this path together, enjoyingeach other's accomplishments, and helping whenneeded. With you by my side, I know no obstacle is insurmountable.

With deepest thanks,

MARIAM

ANNAFADIA

ABOUT THE AUTHOR

Marlene Zaedyan, author of "Nine Lives: Endless Dreams" was born in Lebanon, Beirut. Books were hercompanions and mentors as she grew up amidst the civil war in 1975. She wrote short stories that were never published and were either destroyed orabandoned while seeking refuge.

She has won two awards for her autobiography. Marlene is a beach lover, a multilingual woman, and themother of three young adult children — a girl and two boys with special needs. She admits to being a travelenthusiast and adventurer, and she is amusing and enjoys life. When she is not reading or writing, she issinging and dancing around the island of her cookingcountertop kitchen.

She is married and resides in New England with hertwo special needs sons and an adorable Shih Tzu.

www.ingramcontent.com/pod-product-compliance
Lightning Source LLC
Chambersburg PA
CBHW051512260626
47162CB00008B/2937